The
New Astronomies

Other Books by Ben Bova

THE STAR CONQUERORS

THE MILKY WAY GALAXY

GIANTS OF THE ANIMAL WORLD

THE STORY OF REPTILES

STAR WATCHMAN

THE USES OF SPACE

THE WEATHERMAKERS

OUT OF THE SUN

THE DUELING MACHINE

IN QUEST OF QUASARS

ESCAPE!

PLANETS, LIFE AND LGM

EXILED FROM EARTH

THE FOURTH STATE OF MATTER

THX 1138 (with George Lucas)

THE MANY WORLDS OF SF (Editor)

THE AMAZING LASER

BEN BOVA

The New Astronomies

ST. MARTIN'S PRESS NEW YORK

To Kay and Fred Towers, with many thanks.

Library of Congress Catalog #70-184553
Manufactured in the United States of America

St. Martin's Press
175 Fifth Avenue
New York, N.Y. 10010

AFFILIATED PUBLISHER: Macmillan & Company, Limited, London
—also at Bombay, Calcutta, Madras and Melbourne—the Macmillan
Company of Canada, Limited, Toronto.

Contents

Illustrations

Introduction

New developments in astronomy cascading down upon the contemporary horizon with breathless rapidity have literally overwhelmed all but those intimately concerned with the study of astronomy. An entirely new vocabulary has entered the literature to make itself a part of the new scientific language. New ideas—new thoughts—new speculations have been germinated and brought to fruition, resulting in a reassessment of our concept of the universe and those objects whose totality comprises our universe. What we must recognize is that from a fleeting glimpse of today's universe, scientists have been, and are, attempting to reconstruct its entire history, and the new ideas play a significant role in this history. The speculations associated with these esoteric objects overwhelm the mind and a winnowing process is taking place in an attempt to disclose a pattern which bears some relation to reality. For this reason, there is need for an updating of books on astronomy.

This development was not totally unexpected, for scientists and astronomers knew that with the dawn of the Space Age, when man could project himself and his instruments beyond the veil of the atmosphere, he could illuminate those previously forbidden areas where many secrets of nature lay hidden. Despite this feeling of potential discovery, scientists were still skeptical of what would be found in the depths of space. Until spaceflight began in earnest and until the super radio telescopes could be engineered and erected, there always existed the possibility that their hopes would not materialize. However, developments in this field of space astronomy showed that conclusions drawn by astute and ingenious scientists were founded on firm foundations. Indeed the scientists were proven right to a degree which surprised even the boldest and most daring. Thus, the stage was set for the new astronomies.

As a consequence of these new developments, today we read and hear about quasars, pulsars, neutron stars, black holes, etc. Some of these were highly esoteric concepts only a decade ago and others were not even known at that time. Today, they have become an integral part of our everyday astronomy terminology. The background for the understanding of these new and dramatic facets of astronomy goes back over a half-century, but the assembling of the pieces to provide an understandable picture is as current as today's newspaper. It is this background which provides one of the most fascinating and intriguing stories in all of science. That is what this book is about.

Mr. Bova has skillfully pieced together the elements of the old astronomy to provide an introduction to the new. He has chosen carefully to provide a complete story without again going over background familiar to even the casual reader in astronomy. Therein lies the merit of this book. It is adeptly woven around basic physical principles and current knowledge of astronomy to provide a look into the future and, with this look, to show the posture of astronomy in this last third of the twentieth century. The new astronomy represents a daring flight of human perceptiveness and imagination.

Dr. I. M. Levitt, Vice President
The Franklin Institute
Director-Emeritus, Fels Planetarium

1.

The Three Eras of Astronomy

Atop Mt. Palomar in southern California stands a monument to man's intelligence and curiosity. It is an astronomical observatory, with a telescope that has a 200″ diameter primary mirror. The Mt. Palomar telescope has peered farther into the vast universe than any other optical instrument man has built.

This telescope is named after George Ellery Hale (1868-1938), one of the most respected astronomers of the United States and a driving force in developing the huge telescope and the observatory that houses it.

If Hale were miraculously brought back to Mt. Palomar he would, of course, be elated with the honor his fellow astronomers have given him. And he would be able to use the 200″ telescope without a moment's hesitation. Despite its size, the Hale telescope works very much like optical telescopes in other observatories all around the world.

But there are many astronomers at work today with instruments that Hale would find strange, perhaps incomprehensible.

For example, he would find that about half the world's astrono-

Fig. 1-1. The 200-inch Hale telescope of the Mt. Palomar Observatory (Mt. Wilson and Palomar Observatories)

mers are using giant metal antennae called radio telescopes, and that others are working with equipment in gold mines deep underground to study particles that are being emitted by the Sun. He would see astronomers and engineers working together to place strange instruments on balloons and atop giant rockets.

All these new kinds of instruments and techniques belong to the new astronomies—new ways of investigating the universe—and were mostly undreamed of in Hale's lifetime and before.

Actually, astronomy has gone through three distinct periods, or eras. No one knows when the First Era of astronomy began. It might have been as early as 10,000 years ago when men started making orderly observations of the stars. Certainly men had gazed into the night sky with wonder and awe long before that. By 4000 B.C., when written records began, astronomy was already an important science in Egypt and the other civilized lands of the Middle East.

The Second Era opened in 1609, when Galileo Galilei (1564-1642) built a crude telescope and turned it toward the heavens. For the first time, men weren't limited to studying only what they could see with their unaided eyes. An entirely new view of the universe unfolded, a view that was enormously more grand than anything men had conceived of earlier. Curiously, although we have Galileo's own written testimony of his first telescope observations of the Moon, the planets and the stars, he never said in what month those observations were made. It was sometime between June and September, according to his *Nuncio Siderius,* Galileo's written report of the first telescope observations. The Latin title means "Messenger from the Stars."

The beginning of the Third Era of astronomy is even more difficult to pin down exactly, strange though that may seem. We might say the Era started in 1931, when the first radio telescope observations were reported (they were the result of a lucky accident). We might say it was October 4, 1957, when Russia's Sputnik 1 became the first artificial satellite to orbit Earth. Or July 20, 1969, when Neil Armstrong and Buzz Aldrin made man's first footprints on the Moon.

It is especially difficult to date the start of astronomy's Third Era because there are now so many different astronomies to consider.

Through the First and Second Eras of astronomy, man's study of the outer universe was almost entirely an *optical* study. Astronomers looked at the sky with their unaided eyes or with telescopes. All the information they got came from visible light. The only exception to these optical studies was the study of meteorites—the chunks of stone or metal that fall to Earth from outer space. Meteorites were studied in chemical and geological laboratories. But all the rest of astronomy depended on optical observations of the sky.

In our Third Era of astronomy, scientists have developed instruments and equipment that are capable of "seeing" things our eyes could never detect. Radio telescopes, infrared and ultraviolet instruments, x-ray and gamma ray detectors, neutrino traps—all these innovations tune in on energies and particles that are totally invisible to optical telescopes.

In addition, spacecraft are soaring through the solar system, taking closeup observations of our sister worlds and carrying sensitive instruments through interplanetary space. Rocks and soil from the Moon have been returned to Earth, to be studied by scientists of many different specialties.

Most of this was undreamed of in Hale's time. For the most part, the new astronomies are so new that only a handful of specialists are up to date on the work in each area. And the discoveries are coming so often, the new ideas and new information are bursting on the scene so rapidly, that any book on astronomy is likely to be behind the times in some respects even before it is published.

But no matter if you date the beginning of astronomy's Third Era in 1931 or 1969, the new astronomies have already started to reshape man's understanding of our own planet Earth, the Moon, the solar system and the universe beyond. Astronomers now talk about the solar wind and the magnetosphere, the lunar mascons, the craters of Mars, the greenhouse effect on Venus, Mercury's spin, Jupiter's Van Allen belts, quasars and pulsars and exploding galaxies and stars that disappear into black holes. None of these terms or concepts existed as recently as 1960.

We are going to see what these things mean, and try to learn why astronomy's Third Era is the most exciting one of all.

Someone once said of the famous politician and orator William Jennings Bryan that he was like the mouth of the River Platte: "a mile wide and an inch deep." This book will be wider than it is deep. We will not go into exhaustive detail on every aspect of the new astronomies; rather, we will attempt to highlight the important new ideas that have come to light in astronomy's Third Era so far.

We will begin by taking a very brief glimpse at the first two eras, to understand what they accomplished and how they laid the foundations for today's work. Then we will examine the new astronomies themselves, to see what they are and what they have told us. Finally we will look at the solar system and the universe beyond in the new lights of these new astronomies.

2.

The First Era

It began on the desert.

Thousands of years ago, before men learned how to write, even before there were cities or farms, desert nomads watched the stars.

In the clear still air of the desert, the stars seem very close. They swing through the night sky like a gigantic wheel, rising in the east and setting in the west. They march across the heavens rank on rank, always in the same order, eternal and unchanging.

Yet—there are mysteries in the night sky, mysteries that must have puzzled generation upon generation of desert nomads. For although nearly all the stars keep the same formation year after year, century after century, there are a few that do not; 5 visible stars wander across the sky, blatantly ignoring the unchanging perfection of their fellows. How can that be?

And sometimes a star falls, flashing briefly through the night. A startling thing to see. But more frightening still, once in a great while there is the ghostly apparition of a comet, hanging pale and ominous like a dreadful finger, pointing to some awful disaster that is coming. To say nothing of lunar and solar eclipses, when the Moon slowly fades from sight or turns blood red, or the Sun goes dark and its lifegiving warmth ebbs away. These events must have terrified our ancestors.

As civilization grew and people began to live in cities, some men were able to devote their lives to studying the heavens. Their motives were many, and included both religious and very practical reasons. (Otherwise, why should hard working farmers allow a handful of scholars to waste their time star gazing? Much the same question is still being asked about scientists today!) For those ancient civilizations, quite obviously the people did not regard the study of the stars as a useless waste of time.

To a society based on farming, predicting the seasons is crucially important. Plant too soon and your crops will be killed by late frosts; too late, and the winter will set in before your crop ripens.

There is strong evidence that the immense megaliths of Stonehenge and similar monuments elsewhere in England and France were actually built to serve as astronomical computers of a sort. It is possible to determine midsummer's day, and to predict lunar eclipses, from the arrangement of the stones. Stonehenge was built some 2000 years before Christ, by men who had no cities, no engines, not even iron tools. But they had a desire to predict the seasons accurately, and Stonehenge can still be used for that purpose today.

Even in the very stable climate of Egypt, it was necessary to

Fig. 2-1. Stonehenge. This colossal monument was built in prehistoric times, with little more than human muscle power and crude tools. The stones and circles are arranged to allow predictions of the seasons and eclipses of the Sun and Moon.
(British Department of the Environment)

predict when the Nile River would flood. Astronomers found that when the bright star Sirius rose in the east just before sunrise, the Nile's floods would come soon afterward.

It must have seemed clear to these ancient men that there were powers in the stars that controlled events here on Earth. The sky was where their gods lived, so the motions of the stars were the work of those gods. If someone could interpret what the gods were saying through the movements of the stars and planets, he could help people to live lives more in harmony with the universe. Thus astrology was born hand in hand with astronomy. And it is still with us today.

These earliest astronomers, with only their eyes and a few crude instruments for measuring the angles between stars, could do little more than plot the stellar positions and movements.

Still, they had brains. They were as intelligent as you and I. What they lacked was knowledge, information, data. But they went ahead and built a theoretical picture of how the universe worked. We might laugh at it today, but it was useful to man for thousands of years. If we were thrown on our own into the desert, without modern instruments and knowledge, we might very easily build up the same picture of the universe.

The astronomers of the First Era pictured the sky as a huge bowl hanging over a flat Earth. The stars were specks of fire flecking the surface of the bowl. The Earth was at the center of the universe, flat and unmoving. The stars wheeled around it.

Why? What made them move? What were the stars made of?

These were questions that the First Era of astronomy could not answer. The astronomers simply did not have enough information to answer such questions. But that seldom stops a curious, imaginative man. They invented answers, much in the same way a modern astronomer will construct a theory that tries to explain things that are incompletely understood.

Most of the earliest explanations for the movements of the stars were steeped in religious or superstitious attitudes. But the ancient Greeks began to put matters on a firmer basis. They realized that those few wandering stars did not drift all over the heavens, but stayed to certain paths. The Greeks called them *planetos,* which means travelers. Today we call them planets. Ancient astronomers knew five planets and named them after their gods. We know them today by their Roman names: Mercury, Venus, Mars, Jupiter and Saturn.

All through the long millennia of the First Era of astronomy, men were fascinated by the Sun and Moon, as well as the stars. The Egyptians and many other ancient peoples worshipped the Sun. And well they might, since the Sun is responsible for all life on Earth.

And then there was the Moon. Ever changing, shining, beckoning, the Moon filled the night sky with a mysterious beauty—bright yet cold, distant yet almost close enough to touch. Close enough to touch. How many youths first turned their attention to astronomy because of that lovely beacon hanging before their eyes?

Or maybe the Moon put other thoughts into their heads. After all, just about every culture that has bothered to name the heavenly bodies has given the Moon the name of a beautiful goddess.

By the 2nd century A.D. the ancient land of Egypt had long been dominated by Greek culture. Alexandria was a Greek city built on the Nile delta. No matter that the Romans now held political sway; the culture, the thinking, the ideas of the land were Greek. An Alexandrian astronomer named Claudius Ptolemaeus—known to us now as Ptolemy (died 141 or 151 A.D.)—wrote a book in which most of man's understanding of the heavens was systematically set down and described.

Ptolemy's book is known to us as the *Almagest*. This is an Arabic name. In the violent centuries that followed the collapse of Rome, it was the Arabs who protected the ancient knowledge of the heavens, including Ptolemy's work. Most of the stars we see have Arabic names: Vega, Rigel, Altair, Aldebaran, Betelgeuse, Deneb, to name just a few of the brightest. The Persian Omar Khayyam, known to us mainly for his poetry, was primarily an astronomer and mathematician.

Ptolemy's work summarized most of ancient man's understanding of the heavens. In beautiful detail, he described the appearances of the stars and planets, and tried to explain how the universe was constructed and how it worked. The details of his system—the *Ptolemaic system*—do not really concern us now. Only 2 points need to be emphasized:

1: The so-called Ptolemaic system was not really Ptolemy's invention. He merely put together the work of earlier astronomers and philosophers, most notably the Greek, Hipparchus, who had lived two centuries earlier. But Ptolemy wrote the book that survived the centuries, and his name got the credit, for nearly 1500 years!

2: The Ptolemaic System firmly subscribed to the idea that the Earth stood still and was at the center of the universe. The Sun, Moon, planets and stars all revolved around the Earth. For 1500 years men were content to believe that. This *geocentric* point of view, in fact, is still valid—in teaching the science of earthbound navigation.

And who was the revolutionary who shattered this concept of the universe? Who was the flaming intellectual rebel who flew in the face of common sense and the established order? Who dared suggest that the Earth was not at the absolute center of the universe? A Polish churchman, a quiet, meek man who rarely looked up from his books. Not an astronomer, really; a man so timid that he only allowed his ideas to be published when he was on his deathbed. His name was Nicolas Copernicus.

3.

The Second Era

The First Era of astronomy ended with a flash of brilliance, thanks mainly to 3 great men. The first of these was Copernicus. The others were Tycho Brahe and Johannes Kepler. These 3 produced an accurate description of the way the solar system works—with the planets orbiting in elliptical paths around the Sun. And they did this without the aid of telescopes; it was all based on naked eye observations.

Copernicus (1473-1543) started the revolution by suggesting that the Earth was not at the center of the universe. Intelligent men had known for many years that the Earth is round; the voyages of Columbus and other explorers merely proved it beyond the shadow of a doubt. Copernicus went much further, though, and said that the Earth *moves*! It orbits around the Sun. He had no proof that this was so, but it presented a tidier, more orderly universe than the one outlined in the Ptolemaic view.

Common sense boggled at Copernicus' idea. Obviously the Earth does not move. And just as obviously, the Sun circles around the Earth, as do the stars and planets. Just go out and look! But once

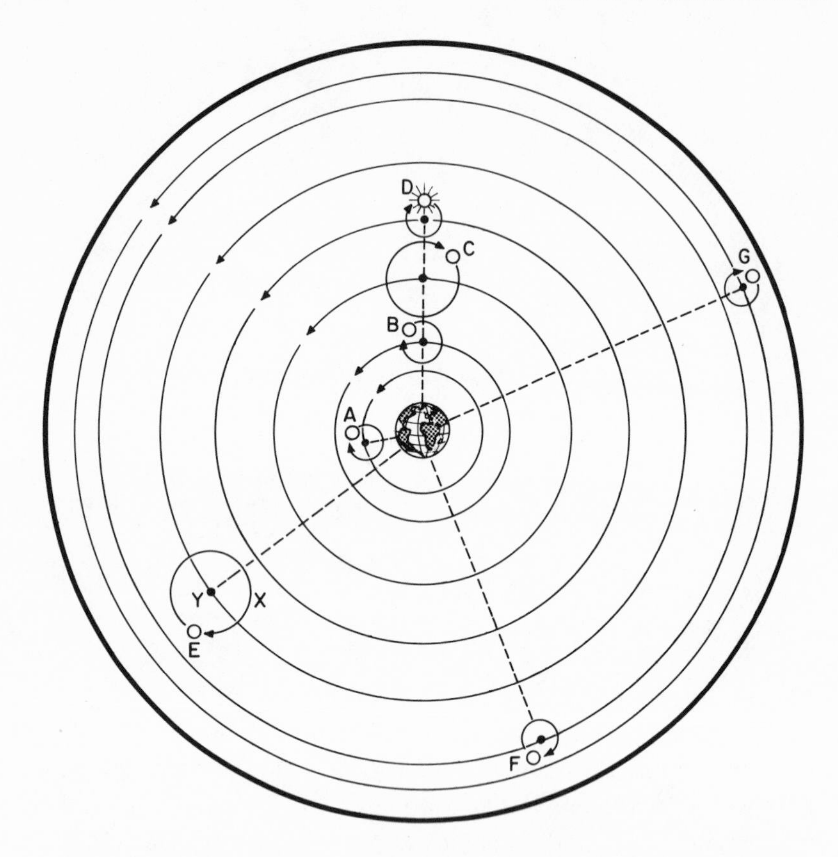

Fig. 3-1. The Ptolemaic view of the universe had the planets revolving around an unmoving Earth. Since actual observations of the planets showed them to be in positions slightly different from those predicted by circular, Earth-centered orbits, astronomers "invented" epicycles, *small circular motions superimposed on the planets' orbits.*

planted, the ideas of Copernicus began to take root. Men argued, sometimes violently. In those 16th century days, astronomy and religion were still very much tied together. And religion was closely linked to the world governments of the time. An "unacceptable" view of the universe could get a man into trouble with the church and the state.

Tycho Brahe (1546-1601) was the son of Danish nobility and the last great observational astronomer of the First Era. He never used a telescope, although he built an elaborate observatory with many measuring instruments on the Danish island of Hveen.

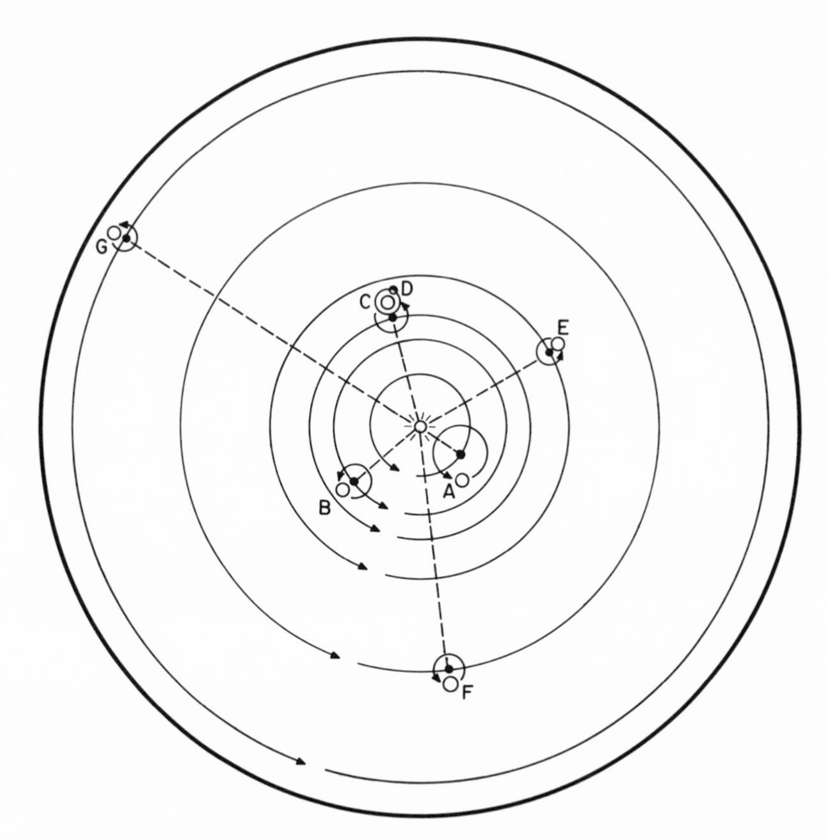

Fig. 3-2. In the Copernican system, the Sun was placed at the center of the solar system. But since Copernicus still believed the planets' orbits were perfect circles, epicycles were still needed. It wasn't until Kepler deduced that the planets moved in elliptical orbits that the need for epicycles was eliminated.

Brahe was no revolutionary, and he never really supported the Copernican view. He *was* the most accurate observer of the time. He devoted his life to determining the exact positions of the stars in the sky, and to mapping out the orbits of the planets with an accuracy that had never been attained before. Tycho found that many of the positions given for the stars in the *Almagest* were sadly in error. He probably thought Ptolemy was a pretty sloppy worker.

Kepler (1571-1630) spent part of his life as Tycho's assistant. Poor eyesight soon made him realize that he would never be a great observational astronomer. So Kepler turned to mathematical studies.

He deduced the true laws of planetary motion; he discovered how the planets orbit around the Sun.

Since ancient times, everyone had assumed that heavenly bodies travel across the sky in perfectly circular paths. After all, everything in the heavens is perfect, and the circle is the perfect shape. (You might wonder why a circle was regarded as more "perfect" than a triangle; so do I.)

This concept was so ingrained in astronomical thinking that when Copernicus arrived at his revolutionary *heliocentric* idea, even he automatically assumed that the planets went around the sun in circular orbits.

When astronomers tried to see if Copernicus' view of the solar system gave a more accurate prediction of the positions of the planets, they found that it did not! In fact, it made scant difference whether the Copernican or Ptolemaic view was assumed—neither one gave a simpler, or more accurate, description of where a given planet would be on a given night.

Kepler changed all that. Using Tycho's painstakingly accurate observations of the path of Mars across the sky, Kepler finally came to the conclusion that the planets go around the sun all right—but not in circles. The shapes of the planetary orbits are *ellipses*.

In great detail, Kepler showed that if you assume the planets follow elliptical orbits around the sun, you can predict accurately and simply the exact position they will be in at any time. This was an

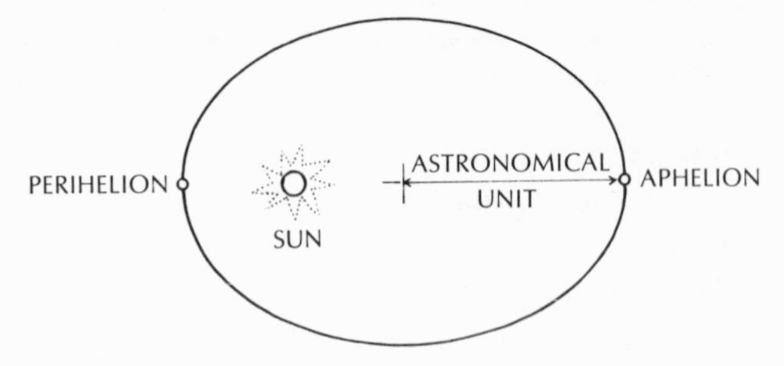

Fig. 3-3. An elliptical orbit, greatly exaggerated to show its difference from a circle. The longest diameter of an ellipse is called the major axis. Half of Earth's major axis is arbitrarily defined as the average Earth-to-Sun distance, and called the Astronomical Unit (AU).

enormous triumph for the First Era of astronomy, although arguments over the geocentric versus heliocentric view still raged on.

The Second Era Begins

Galileo changed all that.

In 1609 his first telescopic observations showed that the heavens are nowhere near as perfect as philosophers had claimed. The Moon is rough and mountainous, not smooth and perfect. There are spots on the Sun—although some critics refused to believe this for years. Most shattering of all, Galileo found four moons orbiting around the planet Jupiter—dramatic proof that not *everything* in the universe revolves around the Earth! He also saw that the planets are not pinpoints of light, as the stars are; the planets show discs, and are other worlds somewhat like our own. And the planet Venus goes through phases of full, quarter, and new (dark) just as the moon does. Copernicus had predicted this as a natural extension of his heliocentric theory.

Galileo's strong evidence in favor of the Copernican view, and his even stronger way of arguing and ridiculing his opponents, got him into trouble with the Roman Catholic Church, which was a powerful political force in Italy. He was forced to renounce his support of the Copernican view. This makes about as much sense as forcing someone to admit that the sky is brown, not blue. Sooner or later the truth becomes painfully obvious.

Astronomers turned to telescopes for a better look at the heavens. The more they saw, the more it became obvious that Earth is not at the center of the universe.

In fact, the astronomers began to find that the universe is enormously larger than anyone had dreamed. As telescopes got bigger and more powerful, millions upon millions of stars became visible. The universe seemed to extend out in all directions, with countless myriads of stars without end.

With telescopes it was possible to see the surfaces of the planets and to study these sister worlds of our solar system. Even in the largest telescopes, though, the stars were still no more than pinpoints of light. This is because they are so far away. Many astronomers guessed that there must be planets orbiting around other stars, but such planets are too small and dim to be seen from Earth, even today.

Isaac Newton (1643-1727) produced one of the major triumphs of science when he discovered the laws of gravity and motion. Kepler had correctly deduced how the planets moved around the Sun. Newton showed why they behave this way—and much more. Newton's laws of gravity and motion are basic to all physics. From the fall of an apple from a tree to the planning of an Apollo lunar mission, Newton's discoveries are fundamental. The principles he discovered are *universal.* His laws of gravity and motion work for all stars everywhere in the cosmos, as far as we have been able to see.

Exploring the Solar System

For several centuries after Galileo's pioneering use of the telescope, astronomers spent most of their efforts exploring the solar system with bigger and bigger instruments. Optics became an ever more crucial part of astronomy. It is no surprise that the era's greatest scientists—men such as Newton himself—were very much involved in understanding the laws of optics and designing better telescopes. Newton himself developed a type of telescope that is still called *Newtonian.*

As telescopes got bigger and better, astronomers found that the solar system—like the universe as a whole—was larger and more complex than naked eye observations had led them to believe.

On March 3, 1781, William Herschel discovered the planet Uranus. Herschel (1738-1822) was born in Germany, but became an astronomer in England under the German-descended king, George III. It is ironic that while most of Herschel's excellent astronomical work produced very little fame for him, the rather accidental discovery of a new planet assured him a place in history.

Herschel's discovery startled the whole intellectual world of Europe. What else was out there, waiting to be discovered?

Newton's laws of motion were used to predict the orbit of the newly discovered planet Uranus. Soon it became apparent that the planet was not following the predicted orbit. Either Newton was wrong, or there was another body—another planet—whose gravitational pull was strong enough to disturb the orbit of Uranus.

In 1843, a young English mathematician, John Couch Adams (1819-1892) used Newton's laws of motion and his own fine brain to predict where the unseen planet must be. He sent his prediction to the Astronomer Royal, George Airy (1801-1892), in the hopes that Airy would locate the planet with one of the large telescopes at the Royal Observatory in Greenwich, England. Airy did not trust the work of such a young man however, and never bothered to search the sky where Adams said the new planet would be. There was a generation gap even then!

Meanwhile the French mathematician Urbain Jean Joseph Leverrier (1811-1877) made a similar calculation and arrived at a very similar answer. He published his work in June, 1846. Airy read Leverrier's report and promptly asked the chief of the Cambridge Observatory to search the area Leverrier had suggested. In a beautiful example of poetic justice the Cambridge astronomer, J. C. Challis (1803-1862), did a rather slipshod job and never discovered the planet. It later turned out that he actually saw it, but did not recognize it as anything more than an ordinary star!

Leverrier meanwhile asked Johann Galle (1812-1910) of the Berlin Observatory to look for the new planet. Galle received Leverrier's request in a letter on September 23, 1846. That same night he found the planet. It was within a few degrees of the location that Adams had originally predicted.

The new planet was named Neptune.

The discovery of Neptune proved that Newtonian physics was right, despite the mess-up in Newton's own country. But after the excitement settled down and the nature of the new planet was determined, astronomers found that Neptune did not account for all the perturbation of Uranus' orbit. There was still something else nudging Uranus slightly out of its predicted path.

Neptune was so distant and swung around in its orbit so slowly that it was going to take many, many years to see if its orbit was also being disturbed. By the beginning of the 20th century, several astronomers had predicted that a 9th planet was out somewhere beyond Neptune.

The American astronomer Percival Lowell (1855-1916) predicted mathematically where the 9th planet would be found, and spent the years from 1906 to his death searching for it. Unhappily, the planet was so small and dim and so far away that it was undistinguishable from the myriad stars Lowell saw through his telescope.

It was not until 1930 that Clyde Tombaugh (born 1906), also an American, finally located the 9th planet. It was named Pluto.

Telescopes had earlier revealed that there are minor planets orbiting between Mars and Jupiter. The first of these was discovered by the Sicilian astronomer Giuseppe Piazzi (1746-1826), shortly after midnight on January 1, 1801. Even the most dedicated astronomers are usually celebrating the arrival of the new year at that time, but Piazzi was a monk as well as an astronomer, and his devotion was rewarded with discovery.

He called the first of these minor planets an *asteroid,* meaning "little star." Today they are also, and more correctly, called *planetoids*. They range in size from dust specks to bodies of rock or metal that are several hundred kilometers across. Some poetic soul once referred to them as "mountains floating loose in space." At first astronomers thought that the asteroids were the remains of a planet that somehow broke apart. Now they mostly feel that the asteroids represent particles of a planet that was never completed, presumably because the gravitational effects of the nearby giant planet Jupiter interfered with the process.

Thousands of known asteroids orbit mainly between Mars and Jupiter. This area is sometimes called the Asteroid Belt, but the idea that these tiny chunks of matter form a barrier in space is just plain wrong. Spacecraft will be able to sail through the so-called belt as if nothing were there—space is so vast that even mountain sized asteroids are trivially small compared to the huge stretches of empty space around them.

Exploring the Stars

While astronomers were mapping out the solar system, they were also using their constantly improved telescopes to probe deeper and deeper into the sky. They found stars, countless stars, in every direction: stars of all colors, giant and dwarf stars, double and multiple stars, clusters of stars, swarms of them.

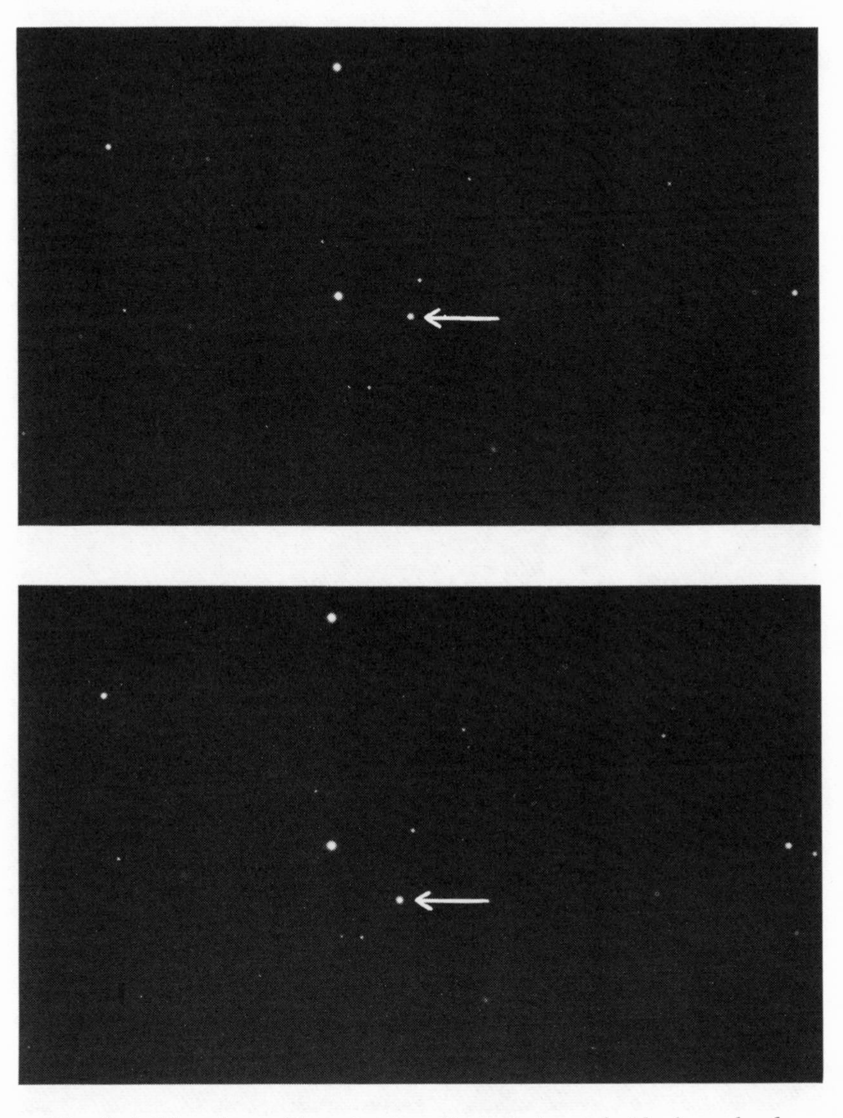

Fig. 3-4. The planet Pluto is virtually indistinguishable from background stars, except that it moves while the stars remained "fixed." These photos show Pluto's motion over a 24-hour period. (Mt. Wilson and Palomar Observatories)

They quickly saw that the Milky Way—that shimmering band of light you can see on a very clear, very dark night—is actually composed of billions of stars. Our own Sun is a member of the Milky Way—is, in fact, a rather ordinary star in it! And they saw other things

Fig. 3-5. The Horsehead Nebula in the constellation Orion shows some of the gas and dust clouds that obscure our view of the central regions of the Milky Way galaxy. (Mt. Wilson and Palomar Observatories)

in space: clouds of shining gas, patches of dust, and fuzzy looking objects that seemed either spindle shaped or elliptical.

By the beginning of the 20th century, it looked as if the Sun was located smack in the center of the Milky Way. Our own Sun, at the center of the Universe? (The Milky Way was then thought to encompass the entire universe.) Most astronomers found this idea very hard to accept. After all, the real lesson of Copernicus had been to get rid of the idea that man's dwelling place was the center of all creation. Our Earth is not the hub of the universe; it is one little planet, a dust speck in the immense cosmos. Our Sun is an average star in every way; why should it be at the center of the universe?

Still, all the best evidence pointed straight to that conclusion.

The evidence consisted of star counts. To determine the size and shape of the Milky Way, and the location of the Sun in it, astronomers counted the stars in every direction around us, to see where they clustered the thickest and where they thinned out. Of course, since there are billions of stars to be seen, counting each one individually is a hopeless task. So astronomers selected small areas of the sky, all the same angular size and carefully spaced through all quarters of the sky. Then they counted the stars in those selected areas.

They found that the Milky Way is a rather flat disc of stars, as you would expect from looking at it with the naked eye. Our solar system is located close to the central plane of this disc; that is why the Milky Way looks like a thin ribbon in our night sky—it is like looking at a saucer with the edge at eye level.

How far does the star-disc extend? Is it farther in one direction than another? Star counts by the best astronomers for generations showed conclusively that the disc of the Milky Way extends for just about the same distance no matter which direction you look in. In other words, the Sun is very near the center of the Milky Way.

The evidence was unarguable. The conclusion was inescapable. But they were all wrong.

It was the American astronomer Harlow Shapley (born 1885) who finally found the true location of the Sun in the Milky Way. He did this in the first two decades of the 20th century.

Shapley noticed that certain huge clusters of stars, globular clusters, seemed to be bunched off in one sector of the Milky Way.

He deduced that these clusters were actually grouped around the true center of the Milky Way. They seem to be off on one side of our sky because we—the solar system—are actually far from the Milky Way's center.

Shapley was basically correct, although it took years of work to prove his point. In a famous debate before the National Academy of Sciences in Washington on April 26, 1920, Shapley argued his case against Heber D. Curtis (1872-1942) of the Lick Observatory. They argued two points: 1: whether or not the Sun is at the center of the Milky Way; and 2: whether or not the Milky Way is the entire universe, or merely one "island" of stars among many.

Curtis argued that the Sun is at the Milky Way's center, but the Milky Way is just one galaxy among a universe full of galaxies. Shapley claimed that the Sun was off to one side of the Milky Way, and that the Milky Way encompassed the whole universe.

The argument was not settled that night—not for years after-

Fig. 3-6. The spiral galaxy in Andromeda, one of billions of galaxies in the observable universe, and a near twin of our own Milky Way. (Lick Observatory)

wards, in fact. Now we know that both men were right on one point and wrong on the other. The Sun is far off to one side of the Milky Way, as Shapley said. But the Milky Way, although huge enough to contain more than 100 billion stars, is only one galaxy in a stupendously enormous universe of galaxies. Actually, those fuzzy spindle shaped and elliptical objects that astronomers had discovered years earlier were other galaxies.

The 100″ telescope on Mt. Wilson went into operation in 1917, and within a few years, shortly after the Shapley-Curtis debate, photographs of the fuzzy "nebulae" showed that they were galaxies of stars, much like the Milky Way, but enormously distant from us. And the farther into space that the telescopes peered, the more galaxies were discovered. There are billions of galaxies, stretching out to the limits our telescopes can reach.

Before we leave the Second Era of astronomy, to view the new astronomies of the Third Era, there are four vital items to inspect.

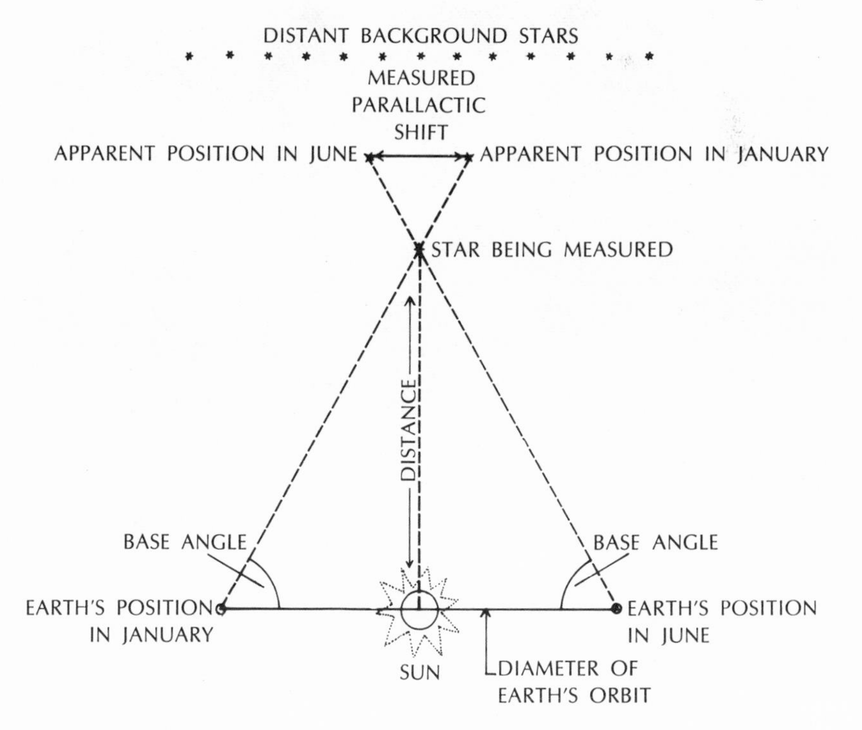

Fig. 3-7. The parallactic shift technique for determining a star's distance.

The Second Era produced 4 key understandings about the size and structure of the universe: 1: measurements of distances to the stars; 2: spectroscopy, by which the physical conditions of the stars could be deduced; 3: nuclear astrophysics, which revealed the energy that makes the Sun and stars shine; and 4: the redshifts of the outer galaxies, which show that the entire universe is expanding.

Fig. 3-8. The parallactic shift of Barnard's Star (lower left) is shown in this triple exposure. Barnard's Star's forward motion through space gives three separate images; the parallactic shift is the small "wobble" in the middle image. More distant stars (upper right) give a single image because they show no detectable motion. (Lick Observatory)

Yardsticks in Space

The distances in space are truly immense.

The Moon, our nearest natural neighbor, is about 240,000 miles (384,000 kilometers) from us. This is 30 times the diameter of the Earth. If we made a circle 1′ in diameter to represent the Earth, the Moon would be a 3″ circle, 30′ away. Try making such a model, and you will begin to understand the enormity of astronomical distances.

Our Earth's average distance from the Sun is some 93 million miles (nearly 150 million kilometers). This distance value has been made into a "yardstick," a unit of measurement, called the *Astronomical Unit*. The AU serves as a convenient unit for expressing distances throughout the solar system. It is much simpler to note that Jupiter, for example, is slightly more than 5 AU's from the Sun than to try to express the distance in miles or kilometers.

When we move out of the solar system to consider the stars the distances become truly mind bending. Units such as miles, kilometers, and even AU's become meaningless. Astronomers have long used a unit called the *lightyear*. The lightyear is a measure of distance, not of time.

It works this way. Light travels through space at the phenomenal

TABLE 3-1: SOLAR SYSTEM DISTANCES

From Sun to:	*In 10^6 km*	*In AU*
Mercury	57.9	0.39
Venus	108.2	0.72
Earth (semimajor axis)	149.6	1.00
perihelion	146.4	0.98
aphelion	151.2	1.01
Mars	227.9	1.52
Jupiter	778.3	5.20
Saturn	1428	9.58
Uranus	2872	19.14
Neptune	4498	30.20
Pluto	5910	39.44

speed of 300,000 kilometers per second (186,000 miles per second). Since there are about 31.5 million seconds in a year, light will cover a distance of 9.45 trillion kilometers (a little less than 6 trillion miles) in one year. Thus one lightyear equals 9.45 trillion kilometers.

But because the term *lightyear* frequently is confused in peoples' minds with time, rather than distance, astronomers prefer to use a unit called the *parsec,* which is equal to 3.26 lightyears. We will see where this strange word, parsec, came from in a moment.

How are these vast distances to the stars measured?

Surveyors use triangulation measurements to determine distances. If a surveyor wants to measure the width of a river, he starts by laying out a baseline along the shore, using for his baseline a chain or line of known length. Next he picks out a target on the opposite side of the river—a tree, perhaps. From each end of his baseline he sights the target tree and measures the angles formed between the target and the ends of the baseline. The longer the baseline, the larger the difference between the two angles and the easier the measurement.

The surveyor then has an imaginary triangle in which he knows the length of the base and the sizes of the two base angles. He can work out the distance from the tree to the baseline by glancing at a trigonometry table.

Astronomers also use trigonometric triangulation measurements when seeking the distance to a star. But because the stars are so far away they need a gigantic baseline; otherwise the angles they are trying to measure would not be different enough from each other to make the measurement work. The whole Earth is not big enough to provide a baseline that can be used for even the nearest stars, so astronomers have turned to a baseline that is literally out of this world: the 300-million kilometer long diameter of the Earth's orbit around the Sun.

An astronomer will photograph the star he is interested in and wait 6 months for the Earth to swing around to the other end of his baseline. Then he photographs the star again, usually on the same photographic plate. Often the astronomer will photograph the star at least once more, so the job usually takes at least a year.

If all goes well, the photographic plate will show at least two different images of the star. There will also be many background stars

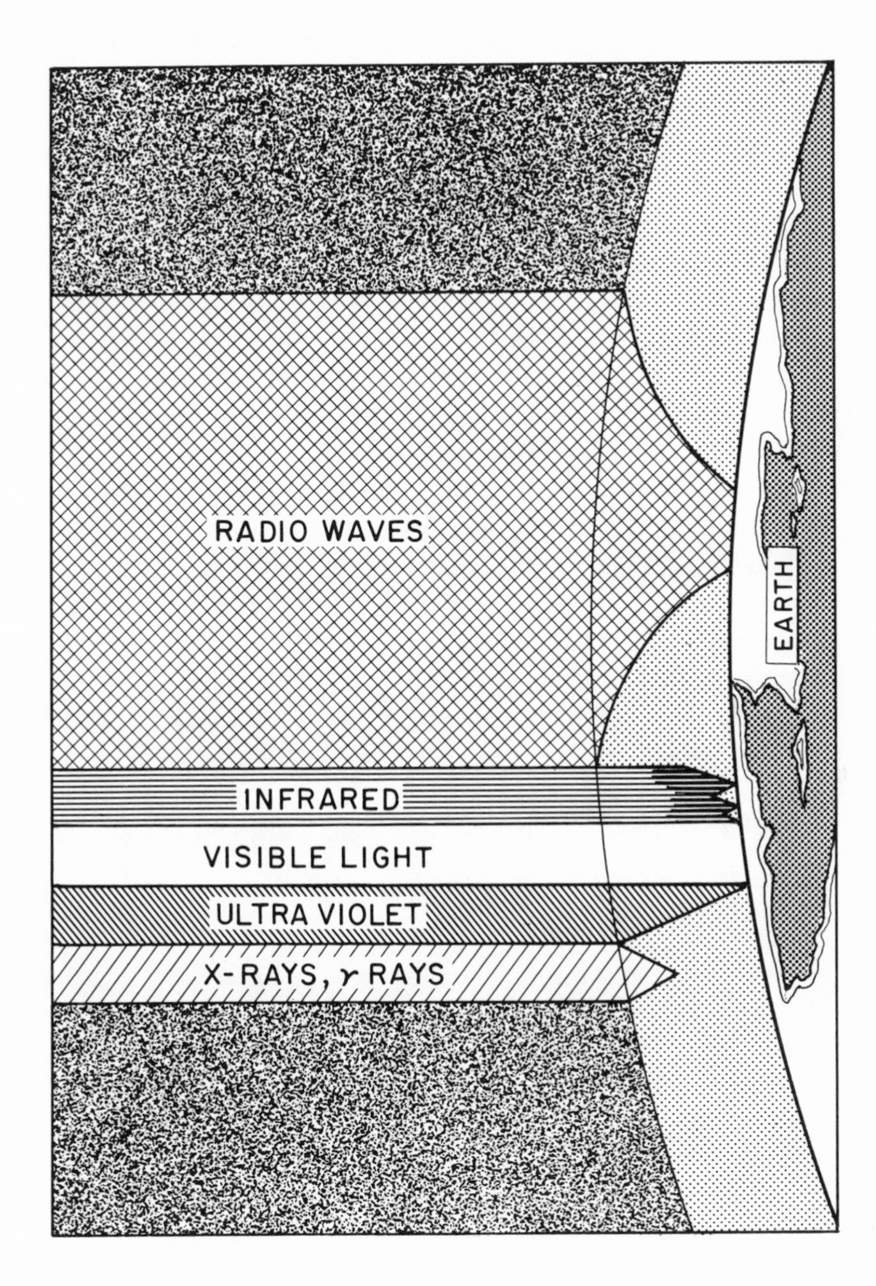

Fig. 3-9. Earth's atmosphere absorbs most of the electromagnetic energy coming from the Sun and stars. Only a portion of the radio, infrared, and ultraviolet wavelengths reach the surface. X-rays and gamma rays are stopped high in the atmosphere. Visible light penetrates the atmosphere completely.

in the picture, but their images should overlap, since they are probably farther away than the target star and show no shift in position. This shift of the target star is called *parallax*.

You can demonstrate a parallactic shift by holding your thumb up at arm's length and squinting at it with one eye at a time. As you switch from one to another, your thumb will seem to move across the background against which you are viewing it. But the shift that your thumb shows is much greater than the parallactic shifts that astronomers get from the stars.

The first successful stellar parallax measurements were made in 1838, although astronomers had been trying to do it almost since the time of Copernicus, 300 years earlier. The big difficulty, of course, as we've said before, was the tremendous distances to the stars, and the extremely small sizes of the angles of their parallactic shifts.

In fact, the triangulation technique works only for the very nearest stars. The farther away a star is, the smaller its parallactic shift. Most stars show no measurable shift at all, they are too distant. Many astronomers have wasted years of time and effort trying to measure the parallax of a star that turned out to be just too far away.

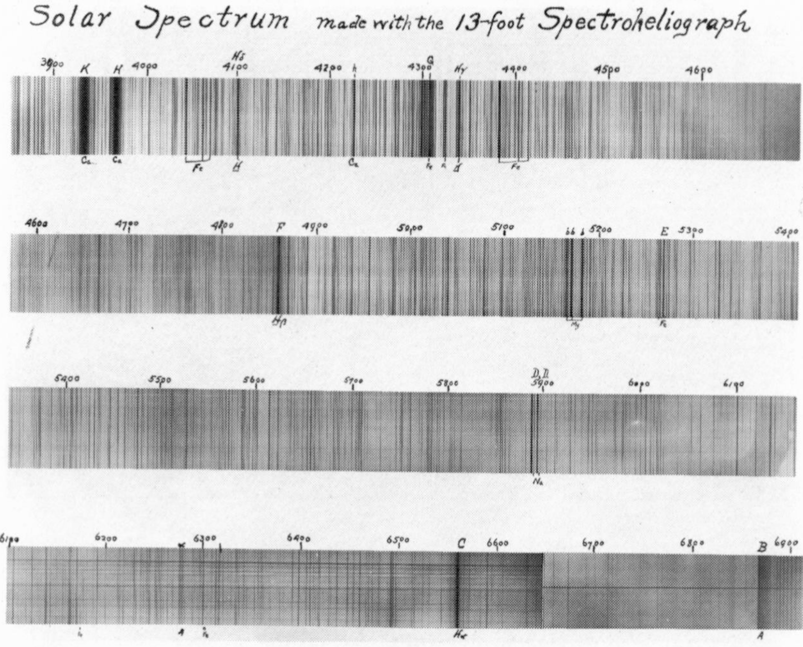

Fig. 3-10. Spectrum of the Sun, showing Fraunhofer lines. (Mt. Wilson and Palomar Observatories)

The first successful measurement of the distance to a star was made in 1838 by Friedrich Wilhelm Bessell (1784-1846) of Prussia. He measured the parallax of the double star 61 Cygni. Its shift is 0.29 second-of-arc. (Degrees of angle are divided into minutes and seconds of arc. One second-of-arc is about the size of a 25¢ coin, at a distance of 3 miles.) The distance to 61 Cygni is 11.1 lightyears.

The largest parallactic shift that has been seen for any star is only 0.76 second-of-arc. This is for Alpha Centauri, which is of course the star that is closest to our solar system. Alpha Centauri is actually a 3 star system; 2 of the stars are quite close together, the 3rd, a faint dwarf star, is about 1/10 of a lightyear closer to the Sun than its 2 bigger companions. Hence it is called *Proxima Centauri.*

The term *parsec* was coined by combining *par*allax and *sec*ond-of-arc. One parsec is the distance an object would be if it showed a parallax of 1 second-of-arc. This distance is 3.26 lightyears. No star has been discovered this close to the solar system; "nearby" Alpha Centauri is 1.3 parsecs or 4.3 lightyears away.

The distance to Alpha Centauri can perhaps be better visualized if you think of the distance between the Earth and the Sun as 1″, and the distance between the Sun and Alpha Centauri as 4.3 miles. By a coincidence, the AU compares to the lightyear almost exactly as the inch compares to the mile.

Because parallactic shifts are so small, reliable triangulation measurements have been made only for a few hundred stars. The technique gives good results down to a parallax of about 0.05 second-of-arc: a distance of 20 parsecs. Beyond that range, other techniques must be used to estimate (not measure) the distances of the stars. Such indirect techniques are not as accurate as the triangulation method, but they are all that can be done with the overwhelming majority of stars.

Fingerprints from Rainbows

Now we come to spectroscopy, a scientific "fingerprinting" technique that allows astrophysicists to determine the chemical elements in a star and much more.

Light from the Sun, or from any natural or artificial source, can be broken up into a *spectrum* of separate colors. Raindrops sometimes break up sunlight and make a rainbow, which is a spectrum. Astronomers use glass prisms or diffraction gratings to "spread out" the light of the sun and stars into rainbow spectra.

When such a prism or grating is attached to an astronomical telescope, the combination is called a *spectroscope*. Instead of giving an image of the object observed, the spectroscope produces a spectrum of the star or planet. Usually the spectrum is recorded on photographic film for detailed study.

In Germany, in 1859, the physicist Gustav Kirchhoff (1824-1887) and the chemist Robert Bunsen (1811-1899) uncovered the laws that govern this behavior of light. They found that a dense object, such as the Sun's main body or a piece of heated, glowing metal will give off a rainbow-like blend of many colors. This is called a *continuous spectrum*.

When ordinary light is passed through a thin gas, however, dark lines show up in the otherwise continuous spectrum. These lines are caused by atoms or molecules in the gas. Different elements and compounds in the gas absorb different wavelengths of light and produce dark absorption lines at specific places along the spectrum. Each

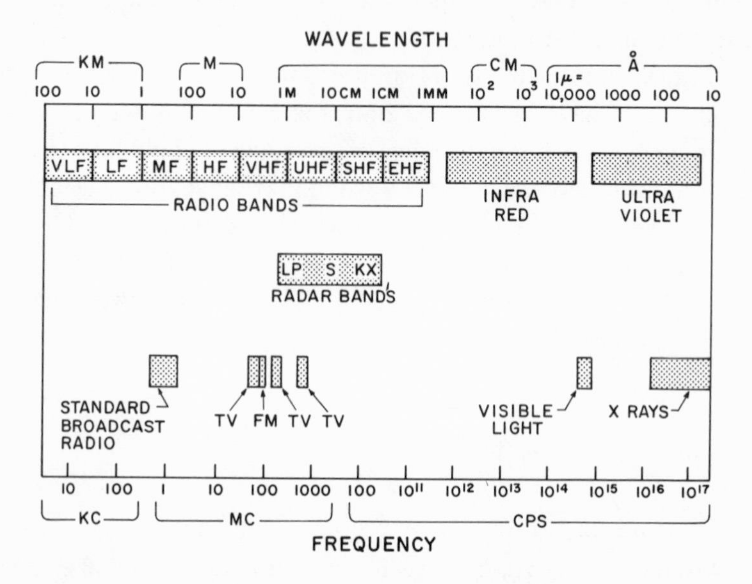

Fig. 3-11. The electromagnetic spectrum extends from radio waves to gamma rays. Visible light is only one small slice of the spectrum.

chemical element produces its own characteristic set of absorption lines, as unique as fingerprints. Thus it is possible to identify the elements in a gas, no matter where it is found in the universe, if the gas is under a condition that produces an *absorption spectrum*.

The surface of the Sun is called the *photosphere*. It is a region of fairly thin gas sitting atop the dense, bright light source of the lower layers of the glowing Sun. The Sun therefore shows a continuous spectrum that is crossed by some 600 dark absorption lines. The German physicist Joseph Fraunhofer (1787-1826) made one of the earliest studies of these lines in 1814, and they are still called Fraunhofer lines today.

Scientists have produced absorption spectra in laboratories, using known elements, and catalogued the wavelengths at which each element produces absorption lines. By comparing the positions of the absorption lines in the Sun's spectrum with known laboratory spectra, astrophysicists have been able to identify more than 60 elements in the sun's photosphere. Any single element will produce more than one absorption line, so there is no one to one matching of the absorption lines in a spectrum and the number of elements present in the light source.

Helium was first recognized as a new element in the Sun's spectrum before it was discovered to exist on Earth; hence its name, from *helios*, the Greek word for Sun. The outermost layer of the Sun is the faint, whispy *corona*, which can only be seen during a total eclipse of the Sun, when the fierce glow of the main body is blocked out by the Moon. The corona's spectrum showed certain lines that could not be identified with any known terrestrial element, and for a while the name *coronium* was proposed. But later it was learned that coronium is actually iron under very unusual conditions, so that its spectral lines were not at first recognized because they did not match laboratory spectra. Now the corona is sometimes called "the Sun's iron crown," although the amount of iron in the corona is actually very little.

Kirchhoff and Bunsen also found that under certain conditions a gas will emit bright lines of color in an otherwise dark spectrum. Here too, the spectral lines can be used as fingerprints: each element produces an *emission spectrum* of bright lines that is unique to itself.

Spectral analysis can also detect compounds, as well as elements.

Elements are composed of individual atoms, or simple molecules made of the same kind of atoms: for example, the oxygen we breathe is in the molecular form O_2, two oxygen atoms linked together. Compounds are molecules of atoms of different elements: hydrogen and oxygen form water (H_2O); hydrogen and nitrogen make ammonia (NH_3); carbon and oxygen can make either carbon monoxide (CO) or carbon dioxide (CO_2); hydrogen and carbon form methane (CH_4).

With the twin tools of spectral analysis and distance measurements, it is possible to deduce a surprisingly large amount of information about the stars. Astronomers can determine a star's true luminosity (the actual amount of light it is emitting), its chemical

TABLE 3-2: ABUNDANCES OF ELEMENTS

Element	*Universe*	*Earth*	*Crust*
H (Hydrogen)	3.5×10^8	—	1,400
He (Helium)	1.4×10^7	—	—
C (Carbon)	38,000	—	27
N (Nitrogen)	83,000	—	3
O (Oxygen)	140,000	38,000	29,500
Ne (Neon)	160,000	—	—
Na (Sodium)	490	130	1,250
Mg (Magnesium)	11,000	15,000	870
Al (Aluminum)	870	350	3,050
Si (Silicon)	10,000	10,000	10,000
S (Sulfur)	4,300	1,800	—
K (Potassium)	66	40	670
Ca (Calcium)	690	330	920
Ti (Titanium)	26	18	133
Fe (Iron)	5,400	13,500	910
Ni (Nickel)	380	1,000	—

The abundances of the elements in the universe at large, in the earth as a whole, and in the earth's crust. The number of silicon atoms is arbitrarily set at ten thousand in all cases, and the values for the other elements computed accordingly. Note that the universe is almost entirely hydrogen and helium, with all the other elements forming a small percentage of "impurity," while the earth is mostly "impurity" (after Brian Mason).

composition, surface temperature, size, spin rate, and even the presence of strong magnetic fields.

Remember that all an astronomer can really see of a star is a pinpoint of light, even in his giant 200″ telescope. Bigger telescopes are better "light buckets;" that is, they can detect very weak light sources and thus see objects that are much farther, deeper, in space than those visible to smaller telescopes. But no telescope can magnify the image of a star to show a noticeable disk. Long exposure photographs often smear out a star's image and make it look like a round, fuzzy disc. But in reality, an astronomer sees no more of a star with even the largest telescope than we do with our unaided eyes.

Thanks to spectroscopy, we know that the Sun is composed almost entirely of hydrogen and helium. And so are the stars, and all the observable universe. Elements heavier than helium make up less than 1% of the universe. Our solid Earth, with its oxygen, carbon, iron, silicon, aluminum, etc., is composed of the "trace elements" of the universe!

The Electromagnetic Spectrum

We have seen that visible light can be broken up into a spectrum of many colors, which range from violet at one end to red at the other.

Thanks largely to the work of the Scottish mathematical physicist

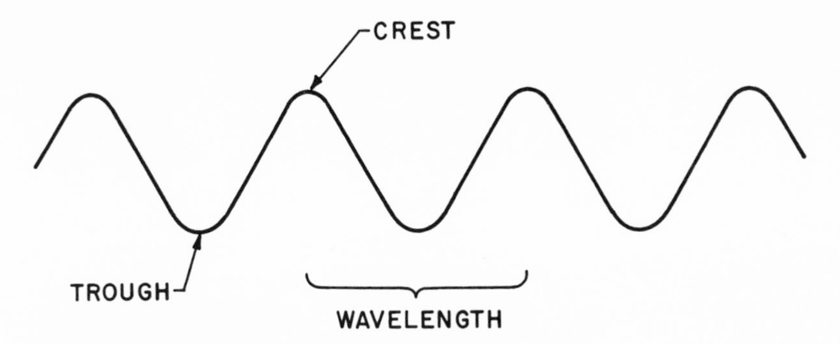

Fig. 3-12. Wavelength is a measure of the distance from one point on a wave to the same point on the next wave, shown here as the distance from crest to crest. Frequency is a measure of the number of waves passing a given point in one second.

James Clerk Maxwell (1831-1879) we know that visible light is a form of electromagnetic energy. In fact, visible light is only one small slice of the huge *electromagnetic spectrum,* which includes radio waves, infrared energy, visible light, ultraviolet, x-rays and gamma rays.

All of these seemingly different forms of energy are actually electromagnetic waves, waves of pure energy. The only difference from one type to another is the wavelength, or frequency. Radio waves are the longest: their wavelengths range from a few tenths of a millimeter out to many kilometers. Light waves are much smaller: more than 10,000 can be packed into a millimeter, the width of the lead in a pencil.

Wavelength, incidentally, is the distance from one energy wave to another, usually measured from crest to crest. Frequency is another way of measuring waves: it is the measure of the number of waves that pass a point in 1 second. You can see that the longer the wavelength, the lower the frequency for any wave.

As we shall soon learn, the Third Era of astronomy is making as much use of the non-visible portions of the electromagnetic spectrum as the first two eras made of visible light. The new astronomies deal heavily in radio, ultraviolet, infrared, x-ray, and gamma radiation —and more, besides!

Energy from the Atom's Nucleus

The sun, as we've said, is a rather average star. It is a ball of hydrogen and helium, mostly, some 1.39 million kilometers in diameter. Its interior temperature has been calculated to be some 20 million degrees.

A few paragraphs ago we talked about the gases that make up the Sun. That was an oversimplification. The Sun is composed of *plasma,* not gas. Plasmas, which have been called "the fourth state of matter," are like gases in some ways, but very different at the same time.

In a gas, the atoms or molecules are electrically neutral. For every negatively charged electron that orbits an atom, there is a positively charged proton in that atom's nucleus.

But in a plasma, the atoms have been *ionized*. That is, one or more electrons have been torn free of the atom. The bereft atom now has a net positive charge, and is called an ion. The free electron still has its negative charge. The plasma as a whole is electrically neutral, since for each electron there is an ion. But those free electrons can conduct electrical currents, and plasmas differ from gases in that plasmas can be affected by electromagnetic forces, where gases cannot be.

The Sun has been glowing steadily for billions of years. Geologists have determined that the Earth is about 4.5 billion years old, and as we will see later, studies of the Moon and meteorites indicate that these bodies are about the same age. Theoretical estimates place the Sun's age between 4 and 5 billion years. Apparently the whole solar system was formed some 5 billion years ago.

Paleontologists have traced life on Earth back at least 2 billion years. If the Sun's output of radiation had changed drastically during all that time, all life might well have been wiped out here. The fact that the oceans have not boiled away or frozen completely shows that the Earth's temperature has remained within a fairly narrow range —only 100°C separate boiling from freezing. Thus the Sun's heat output must have remained almost perfectly constant for billions of years.

What is the source of this unfailing energy? When scientists first began to realize, in the latter half of the 19th century, that the Sun is billions of years old, this question became crucially important. The Sun pours out the energy equivalent of more than 10^{10} megatons of TNT exploding every second—10 billion megatons! Every second! And this has gone on for billions of years!

In the 19th century, nothing known to man could account for this fantastic energy production. If the Sun were a mixture of pure carbon and oxygen, for example, and burned like a coal flame, it would burn itself out within a few thousand years. Several astronomers considered the possibility that the Sun might be slowly shrinking and converting gravitational energy into heat. But calculations showed that this energy source would have lasted only a few million years.

By the 1930s physicists were probing the nucleus of the atom and finding enormous energies there. In 1938, Hans Bethe (born 1906), who had come to America from Germany, and Carl F. von Weizsacker (born 1912), in Germany, both worked out the basic principles of nuclear energy production in the Sun. Neither man knew of the other's work at the time. Bethe received the Nobel Prize in physics for this work in 1967.

The principle of nuclear energy is summarized in Einstein's equation $E=mc^2$. That is, energy can be produced from matter. Under proper conditions matter can be converted into energy and *vice versa;* in fact, matter and energy are fundamentally the same thing.

Here on Earth, the two seem quite separate and distinct. Matter is one thing and energy is another. But in the core of the Sun, where temperatures reach 20 million degrees or more, *nuclear fusion* reactions that change matter into energy can easily take place.

The plasma at the Sun's core is completely ionized; there are no neutral atoms present, they have all been stripped down to bare

TABLE 3-3: HYDROGEN FUSION PROCESSES

Carbon Chain

$H^1 + C^{12} \rightarrow N^{13} + y$
$N^{13} \rightarrow C^{13} + e^+ + v$
$C^{13} + H^1 \rightarrow N^{14} + y$
$N^{14} + H^1 \rightarrow O^{15} + y$
$O^{15} \rightarrow N^{15} + e^+ + v$
$N^{15} + H^1 \rightarrow C^{12} + He^4$

Proton-Proton Reaction

$H^1 + H^1 \rightarrow H^2 + e + v$
$H^2 + H^1 \rightarrow He^3 + y$
$He^3 + He^3 \rightarrow He^4 + 2H^1$

Key

H^1 = Hydrogen (proton)
H^2 = Deuterium (deuteron)
He^3, He^4 = Helium isotopes
C^{12}, C^{13} = Carbon isotopes
N^{13}, N^{14} = Nitrogen isotopes
O^{15} = Oxygen isotope
e^+ = positron (positive electron)
y = gamma ray
v = neutrino

Two nuclear fusion processes for converting hydrogen to helium, releasing energy in the form of gamma rays and neutrinos. Note that in the carbon chain, only four hydrogen nuclei (protons) and one carbon nucleus are required as input; the carbon nucleus, after several transmutations, returns to its original form at the chain's end. In the sun, the proton-proton reaction produces most of the energy. Carbon chain reactions are more important in hotter stars.

nuclei and free electrons. Four hydrogen nuclei (single protons) engage in reactions that produce a helium nucleus (two neutrons and two protons). The helium nucleus is 0.7% lighter than the four original hydrogen nuclei. This amount of mass is converted into energy, the energy we receive here on Earth as sunshine.

Although 0.7% is a small amount of mass to account for the Sun's huge energy output, it means that the Sun is converting about 4 million tons of matter into energy every second. The Sun has been shedding mass at this rate for billions of years. Yet, if all the hydrogen in the Sun were changed to helium, the Sun would be only 0.7% lighter than if it were pure hydrogen.

The Sun, then, is a thermonuclear reactor. It produces energy in much the same way that an H bomb produces an explosion: through thermonuclear fusion. But the Sun and stars do it in a controlled manner.

As astrophysicists unravelled more and more about the nuclear energy processes in stars, they began to see how and why stars go

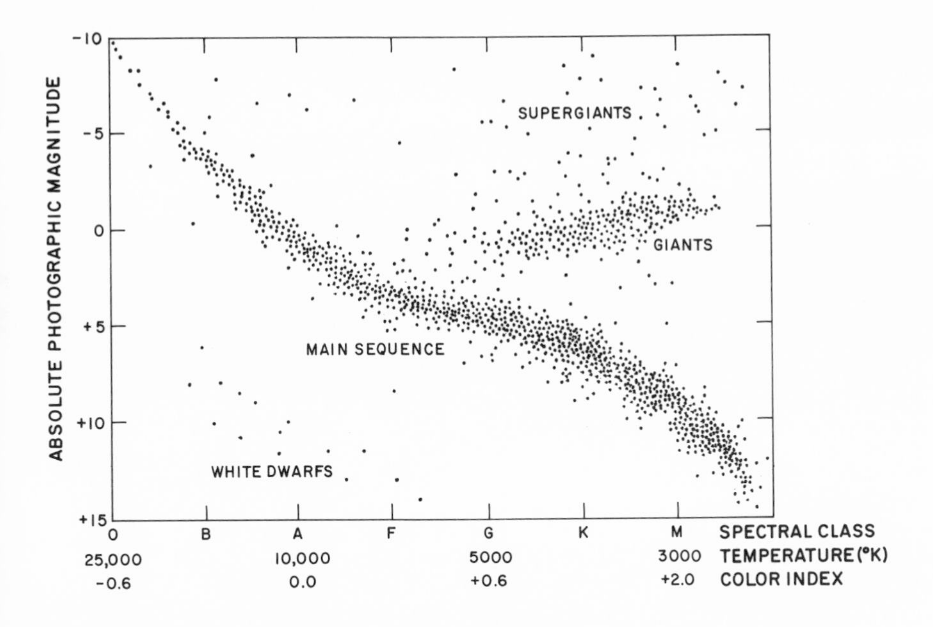

Fig. 3-13. The Hertzsprung-Russel diagram plots the brightness of stars against their temperatures. Stable stars such as the Sun fall into the Main Sequence family. As stars age, they move into the Giant, Supergiant and White Dwarf stages.

through definite life spans. As we will see in Chapters 8 and 9, stars are born out of vast clouds of interstellar plasma and dust, go through a long phase of stability such as the Sun is now enjoying, then begin to change into red giants, become unstable, explode, and finally end as white dwarf stars, or neutron stars—or they disappear from the universe altogether!

During a star's lifetime, the nuclear energy processes going on in its core "cook" constantly heavier elements. Hydrogen is turned into helium; later helium undergoes thermonuclear fusion reactions

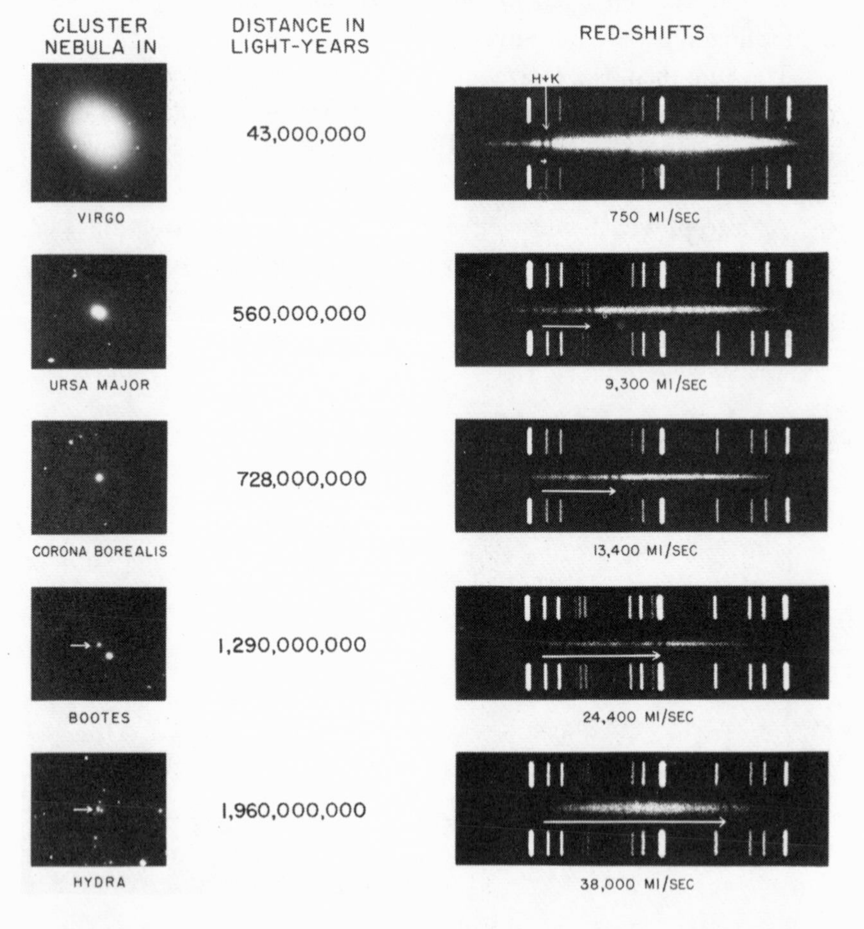

Fig. 3-14. The galaxies outside the Local Group all appear to be moving away from us, and show redshifts in their spectra, which have been related to their distances. (Mt. Wilson and Palomar Observatories)

that produce carbon, oxygen and neon; then heavier elements are produced. Cosmologists are now almost totally agreed that the present shape of the universe can be explained by assuming that nothing existed originally except hydrogen: stars have "cooked" all the other elements and then spewed them out into space in the explosions that mark a star's death throes.

The first stars of our Milky Way galaxy, then, may have started out with nothing but hydrogen. They produced helium and some heavier elements, then blew these elements out into space when they exploded. This material became the building matter for new stars. Our Sun, which has nearly 1% of its mass in elements heavier than helium, is probably a third generation star. There must have been two earlier generations or more to "cook" the elements that the Sun now contains.

Redshifts and the Expanding Universe

In 1929 the American astronomer Edwin P. Hubble announced that most of the galaxies beyond the Milky Way have spectra that are shifted toward the red end of the spectrum. This redshift was immediately assumed to be a *Doppler shift*, and was taken as evidence that the entire universe is expanding.

Christian Doppler (1803-1853), an Austrian physicist, suggested in 1842 that light would shift toward the red end of the visible spectrum if the source of light is moving away from the observer, and toward the blue end of the spectrum if the light source is moving toward the observer. This is very much like the change in pitch of a train whistle or ambulance siren as it approaches and then passes and goes away from you.

Thus when Hubble announced that the other galaxies showed spectral shifts toward the red, astronomers and cosmologists agreed that the universe must be expanding. The redshifts meant that the galaxies were moving away from each other. No one was suggesting that the Milky Way was the center of the universe, or that the galaxies were leaving us. If we could be transported to a distant galaxy and look at the sky from there, it would seem that our new galaxy was standing still and all the others—including the Milky Way—were rushing away. The entire universe is expanding.

One way to picture this expansion is to imagine a balloon speckled with dots. As the balloon is inflated, each dot moves farther away from the other dots. The balloon's skin is expanding. And so is the fabric of our universe, according to modern cosmological theory.

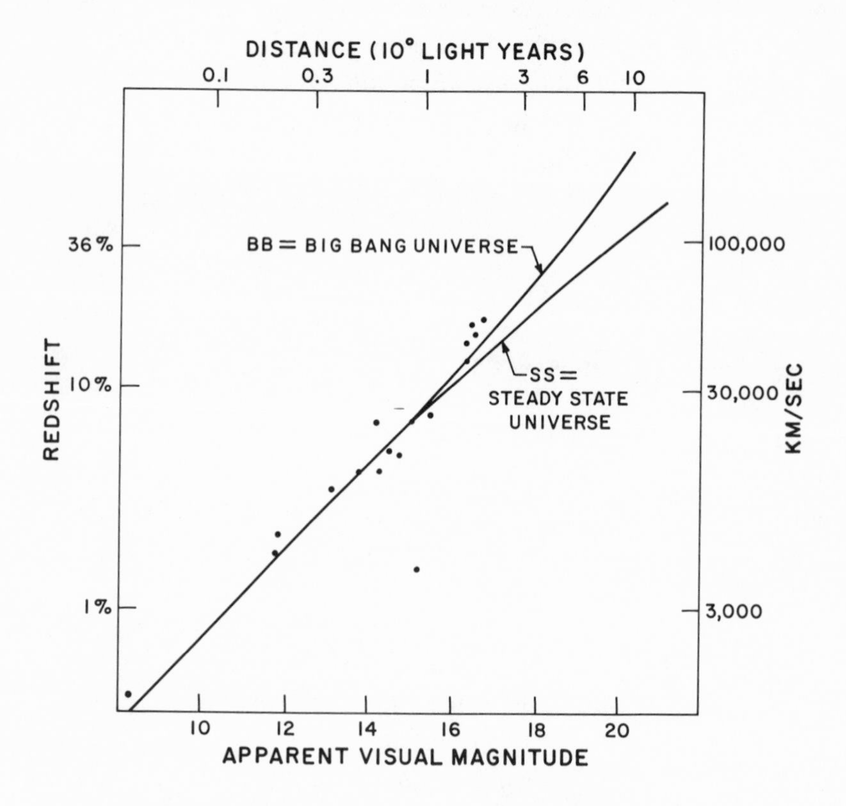

Fig. 3-15. The relation of redshift to brightness (and hence, distance) for the galaxies outside the Local Group apparently follows a straight line, called the Hubble Relationship. If the universe began in a single explosion, as the Big Bang theory demands, then the farthest galaxies should diverge from this straight line and follow the curve labelled BB. If the universe has always been much the same as it is now, as the Steady State theory claims, then the SS curve should be the one the farthest galaxies would follow. The quasars, which may be the farthest objects yet observed, do not follow either of these rules and cannot be plotted on a simple curve.

There are clusters of galaxies that are holding together and moving as groups. Gravitational forces hold such clusters together; apparently over ranges as large as tens of millions of parsecs, gravity is a stronger force than the force that is causing the expansion. But over billions of parsecs, expansion is the dominant force. Our own local group of galaxies is holding together.

Hubble also showed that the farther away a galaxy is, the faster it is flying away from us. That is, the fainter and presumably farther galaxies show larger redshifts.

This *Hubble relationship* of brightness versus redshift produced a neat, straight line when plotted on a graph. It looked as if the universe were expanding smoothly: the farther away the galaxy, the greater its speed of recession. This relationship held true for the billions of galaxies that could be seen in the Mt. Palomar telescope.

Then in 1960 the *quasars* were discovered, thanks to radio astronomy. They show huge redshifts, greater than any galaxy's. And they do not behave in the way galaxies do, not at all. They apparently make a shambles of the Hubble relationship, and have given astronomers and cosmologists alike the nervous fidgets. More on the quasars in later chapters.

The Universe of the Second Era

The Second Era of astronomy mapped out the solar system, the Milky Way galaxy, and the universe at large—although the true extent and shape of the universe are still in considerable doubt. And the Second Era also uncovered the basic physical behavior of the stars and galaxies. The combination of astronomy and physics into the discipline of *astrophysics* proved to be a powerful tool for understanding the workings of the heavens.

However, by the third decade of the 20th century, it had become quite clear to astronomers that they faced an impassable roadblock in their studies of the Milky Way.

Our galaxy, like many others, is strewn with grains of dark material that astronomers call *interstellar dust*. It was this dust that confused the star counts before Shapley. As astronomers look out along the plane of the Milky Way, the dust obscures the light from the more distant stars. This is why it seemed that the star counts petered out rather evenly in all directions around us. Shapley was able to see the much more distant globular star clusters because they are riding high above the Milky Way's central plane, clear of the obscuring dust lanes. And the still farther external galaxies can be seen easily —except along the Milky Way's central plane, where the dust clouds are.

Sadly, astronomers resigned themselves to the fact that they would never see the central regions of the Milky Way, where the stars are clustered thickly, and where the oldest stars in our galaxy must be. Optical astronomy had reached its limits, they realized.

What they did not realize was that the new astronomies were just getting started!

4.

The Third Era Begins

There is no magic date at which the Second Era of astronomy ended and the Third Era began. As we saw in Chapter 1, the transition between the two was actually rather gradual, taking place more or less over a span of some 30 years.

For the sake of convenience, though, we can pick World War II as the dividing mark. That war began in 1939 and ended in 1945. Before the war, astronomy was still in the Second Era, although the first glimmerings of the new astronomies were already being made. After the war, the new astronomies became the major concern of most astronomical research, and the Third Era was upon us.

The war itself stopped almost all astronomical work, but it helped astronomy in some indirect ways. For one thing, the war forced scientists and engineers to push hard on the development of electronic equipment. Better and more reliable radios, new and sensitive radars and other electronic gear became vital to the war effort. As we will soon see, this sensitive electronic equipment gave astronomers a new way to investigate the heavens—radio telescopes and radar.

The war also forced development of rocket boosters, such as

Germany's dreaded V-2. Twelve years after the guns fell silent, man's first artificial satellite went into orbit. And twelve years after that, man stepped onto the Moon. Rocket borne instruments have given astronomers a much better look at the universe than they ever had before.

Optical Telescopes

It would be a mistake to think that the new astronomies of the Third Era have crowded out the long standing champion of astronomers, the optical telescope.

Far from it. For one thing, new and improved optical telescopes of many types are still being built. For another, the well proven optical telescope is being mated to electronic "boosters" that improve its seeing power. And optical telescopes are also being placed in high altitude balloons and aboard satellites to get them above Earth's atmosphere, where they can see better.

The air that looks so clear to us is little more than a murky blanket to the optical astronomer. The air is filled with clouds that muffle his telescope. And even on the clearest, darkest, and calmest of nights, the atmosphere always filters out much of the energy that comes from the stars and dims the light that does get through. In daytime it is impossible to see anything except the Sun, and sometimes the Moon and the planets Venus and Mercury. Even at night the sky is never completely dark; there is always some sky glow that interferes

TABLE 4-1: LARGE OPTICAL TELESCOPES

Size (inches)	*Location*	*Date of Construction*
236	Russia	Under construction
200	Mt. Palomar, USA	1948
152	British Columbia, Canada	planned
150	New South Wales, Australia	planned
144	La Silla mountain, Chile	Under construction
120	Lick Observatory, USA	1959
102	Crimean Observatory, USSR	1960
100	Mt. Wilson Observatory, USA	1917

with the most sensitive observations. And more recently, air pollution has added to the astronomers' woes.

The 200″ Hale telescope at Mt. Palomar went into operation in 1949. A 236″ telescope is under construction in Russia. These may well be the largest optical telescopes ever to be built on Earth. The reason for this is not a limitation on the sizes that can be built; the main trouble lies in the nature of our atmosphere.

Because our air is murky and turbulent, astronomical observatories are usually placed on mountaintops, where they are as far removed as possible from clouds and weather, from the general haze and turbulence of the atmosphere, and from the glare, dust and smog of cities. Still, this is not good enough. For one thing, cities have a way of growing and creeping up on observatories. More than one observatory in the United States has been rendered useless because the noisy, bright, dirty city encroached on it. Even the Mt. Wilson observatory, where the famous 100″ telescope is housed, is becoming gradually less and less useful because sprawling Los Angeles is getting in the way.

But there is a still more fundamental problem that limits the useful size of an optical telescope. The problem is the atmosphere's inherent turbulence. Due to the Sun's heating and our planet's spin, the atmosphere is always moving. Even at the top of the tallest mountains, the air is not still. A telescope must look through many kilometers of air, all of it in constant motion. This turbulence of the atmosphere is what causes stars to twinkle when we look at them. To an astronomer with a very sensitive telescope this twinkling effect is magnified to the point where the star he is trying to study will fade in and out of focus, and even jump right out of the telescope's field of view.

Optical astronomers refer to the general conditions of the atmosphere as "seeing." When the seeing is good, stars appear as sharp points in the telescope; great detail can be seen of the surface of the Moon; even the more distant planets can be seen with some detail. When the seeing is bad, the stars jiggle madly and appear as fuzzy "golf balls;" the Moon and planets become blurred.

These problems actually get worse with bigger telescopes. A bigger telescope can gather in more light than a smaller one, and therefore can peer deeper into the universe. But it also focuses down on a smaller area and becomes more sensitive to bad seeing. This is one major reason why it now seems that 200″ telescopes will be the largest ever built. On Earth.

Electronic "Boosters"

Telescopes by themselves extend man's eyesight far beyond the power of his unaided eyes. The Mt. Palomar "light bucket" can detect images that are 10 million times too faint for our eyes.

There are other pieces of equipment that make telescopes even more useful. Spectroscopes dissect and analyze the light a telescope brings in, and cameras are now used to do almost all the actual observational work.

The human eye is a better light gatherer than any camera, but the camera can stand on duty for hours without blinking, long after a man's eyesight would begin to blur from fatigue. And long exposure photographs can build up images of extremely faint stars; sometimes the camera is left open all night, then shut, and then reopened on the same scene the following night.

More recently, electronic "boosters" have entered the optical observatories. The heart of all these *photoelectric* devices is the photoelectric cell, the same sort of "electric eye" that opens supermarket doors when you step through a beam of light. The photoelectric cell converts light energy into an electrical current, in direct proportion. Thus, x amount of light produces x amount of electrical current. Twice x of light yields twice x of electricity, and so on.

The simplest use of the photoelectric cell is as a photometer, or light counter. The cell will give a very precise measure of the amount of light coming into the telescope. Thus astronomers can make very accurate measurements of the intensity of light being given off by objects in space.

To measure the light from an extremely faint source, such as a distant galaxy, we add a photomultiplier to the telescope. Basically, this is much like the photometer, except that the photomultiplier can produce a much stronger electrical current than the incoming amount of light would give in a simple photometer. In a photomultiplier, the light energy can be translated into an electrical current that is a million times stronger than the original light energy. With the photomultiplier's power of multiplication known and under careful control, very faint objects can be studied and their light output determined conveniently and precisely.

The photometers and photomultipliers give their information in the form of a meter reading, a pointer on a dial, a number. In recent years, photoelectric techniques have been developed to produce images—something like television pictures—that are much better than anything the telescope can produce by itself. The images can be displayed on a screen, or recorded on film or video tape.

The light coming in from the telescope is "boosted" (astronomers prefer to say "enhanced") by photoelectric means, and the flow of electrons that the light yields is then made to produce an image much in the same way that your television set turns electrons into pictures.

With electronic enhancement, a telescope can produce photographs many times faster than with a simple optical camera, because the sensitivity of the telescope-booster-camera combination is much higher than the sensitivity of the telescope and camera by themselves. But more importantly, the booster can increase the effective light gathering power of the telescope. In early experiments of such techniques, telescopes of 40″ to 60″ in diameter obtained photographs that rivalled those produced by 100″ telescopes.

While it still seems that 200″ telescopes are up against the basic limitations of the atmosphere, and cannot be made to do much better even with electronic boosting, photoelectric enhancement techniques will be extremely useful for smaller telescopes; they will see much farther into the heavens than their designers dared to dream.

The First Radio Telescopes

The first of the new astronomies began as an accident.

In 1931, the Bell Telephone Laboratories assigned one of their young radio engineers, Karl Jansky (1905-1950), the task of tracking down some of the sources of electrical interference—"static"—that often bothers long distance radio communications.

To find where the interference was coming from, Jansky put together a radio receiver and an antenna that could be swivelled around and pointed at different locations. He originally thought that the "static" was coming from electrical disturbances high in the Earth's atmosphere. There are regions of the atmosphere at altitudes between 80 and 400 kilometers where layers of ionized gases—plasmas—reflect and absorb radio waves. This whole area is called the *ionosphere.* Jansky thought ionospheric disturbances were causing the "static" he was after.

Fig. 4-1. An early type of dipole array radio telescope, the Mills Cross. (Division of Radiophysics, C.S.I.R.O., Australia)

By 1932, he had found that there was indeed a source of "static" at a wavelength of 14.6 meters coming from the sky. His antenna picked it up rather easily. But it did not seem to be coming from anywhere in the atmosphere. The source of the interference rose in the morning, crossed the sky from east to west, and set at dusk. Jansky thought the source was the Sun.

But wait. He soon noticed that the interference source rose above the horizon a few minutes before the Sun and set a few minutes before the Sun. Puzzled, Jansky continued tracking the radio source and found that it crossed the sky in 23 hours, 56 minutes.

Jansky was no astronomer. So he set about to teach himself some astronomy. He soon learned that the stars themselves go across the sky in 23 hours, 56 minutes.

Without knowing it, Jansky had built the first radio telescope.

By 1936, another American radio engineer, Grote Reber (born 1911) had built the first true radio telescope. It had a parabolic curved "dish" antenna 30′ (9.1 meters) in diameter that could be steered to point anywhere in the sky. It received radio signals of 2 meters' wavelength.

Like Jansky, Reber found that some parts of the sky were more intense sources of radio "noise" than others. In particular, the region around the constellation Sagittarius seemed to be the strongest source of radio signals. Optical astronomers had determined earlier in the 20th century that this was the region in which the center of the Milky Way galaxy lay.

We should point out right now that the radio emissions received by radio astronomers are perfectly natural in origin.

As we saw in Chapter 3, radio frequency energy is part of the electromagnetic spectrum, just as light is. Radio waves are electromagnetic energy of much longer wavelength and lower frequency than visible light. The Sun and stars emit radio wavelength energy, as well as light and many other forms of electromagnetic energy.

The Sun and the stars that are familiar to us in the night sky emit relatively little radio wavelength energy. Their output of visible light is much stronger. But there are other objects in the sky, as we will soon see, that emit much more radio energy than light. In fact, many of these radio sources are absolutely invisible to optical telescopes.

5.

A New Window: Radio and Radar Astronomy

As we saw in Chapter 4, astronomers generally regard Earth's atmosphere as something between an irritation and a curse. Our turbulent air absorbs light from the stars and causes poor seeing conditions more often than not.

And this is for the wavelengths of visible light, where the atmosphere is transparent! Many other wavelengths, such as ultraviolet and x-ray, are almost completely blocked by the atmosphere.

But Jansky found that at least some radio wavelengths get through the atmosphere. He discovered a new "window" through which we can look out on the universe. Radio signals of wavelengths from about 0.25 centimeter to roughly 30 meters can get through this atmospheric window and reach our planet's surface. Longer wavelengths are blocked by the ionosphere; we will look at the shorter wavelengths in the next chapter.

Radio engineers and astronomers have a jargon of their own. The shortest wavelengths, from 3 millimeters to 1 meter, are called *microwaves*. There are also terms such as:

millimetric, for wavelengths of 1 mm to 1 cm
centimetric, for wavelengths of 1 to 10 cm
decimetric, for wavelengths of 10 cm to 1 meter
metric, for wavelengths of 1 to 10 meters
decametric, for wavelengths of 10 to 100 meters, and so on.

Radio astronomy is so new—it began in earnest only after the end of World War II—that most of the big discoveries in the field have come from building new radio telescopes that can pick up wavelengths that the older instruments could not reach. Thus, the radio exploration of the universe has been in large part an exploration of the radio wavelengths that can be detected through our atmospheric window.

How a Radio Telescope Works

Basically, a radio telescope works in much the same way as an optical telescope: it gathers in electromagnetic energy. Instead of using lenses or mirrors that are sensitive to the wavelengths of visible light, radio telescopes use antennae and parabolic reflectors made of metals that are sensitive to radio energy.

And since the radio wavelengths being used are some 100,000 times longer than the wavelengths of visible light, radio telescopes must be larger than optical instruments. Typically, where optical telescopes are measured in inches or centimeters, radio telescopes span feet or meters. Thus the 200″ Mt. Palomar telescope has its radio equivalent in the 300 meter "dish" at Arecibo, in Puerto Rico.

Not all radio telescopes use parabolic dishes for their antennae. Many use a type of antenna that is called a *dipole array*. This looks like a series of metal poles, something like TV antennae, stuck into the ground over distances of hundreds of meters. Dipole arrays are often arranged in **x** or **|** shapes.

The big curved metal dishes are usually steerable, so that they can be pointed to different parts of the sky.

Regardless of its shape or size, the antenna of a radio telescope corresponds to the lens or mirror of an optical telescope. The antenna gathers the invisible radio waves. The incoming signal is then transformed into an electrical current, just as in any radio receiver. The current is then usually hooked into some sort of recording system, such as a pen and ink graph on a revolving drum, which traces out a continuous diagram showing the intensity of the incoming

Fig. 5-1. A steerable antenna radio telescope, the 60-foot "dish" at Harvard College Observatory's Agassiz Station in Massachusetts. (Harvard College Observatory)

signal. So although radio astronomers speak of "signals" and "noise" from the stars, they do not actually listen to the radio emissions from the heavens. They chart them on graph paper, usually.

One of the original problems with radio telescopes was their relative lack of *resolving power*. That is, radio telescopes could not pinpoint the location of an object in space. Good optical telescopes can resolve angles of about 0.05 second-of-arc: they can discriminate two separate objects separated by that tiny amount. Conversely, they can pinpoint the location of an object in the sky to that accuracy.

Since radio telescopes are dealing with much longer wavelengths, they cannot obtain comparable resolutions. The first large radio telescopes built shortly after World War II had resolving powers of about 1 minute-of-arc. By 1960 this had been reduced to about 1 second-of-arc.

But although a *single* radio telescope cannot match the resolving power of an optical instrument, radio telescopes can be used together

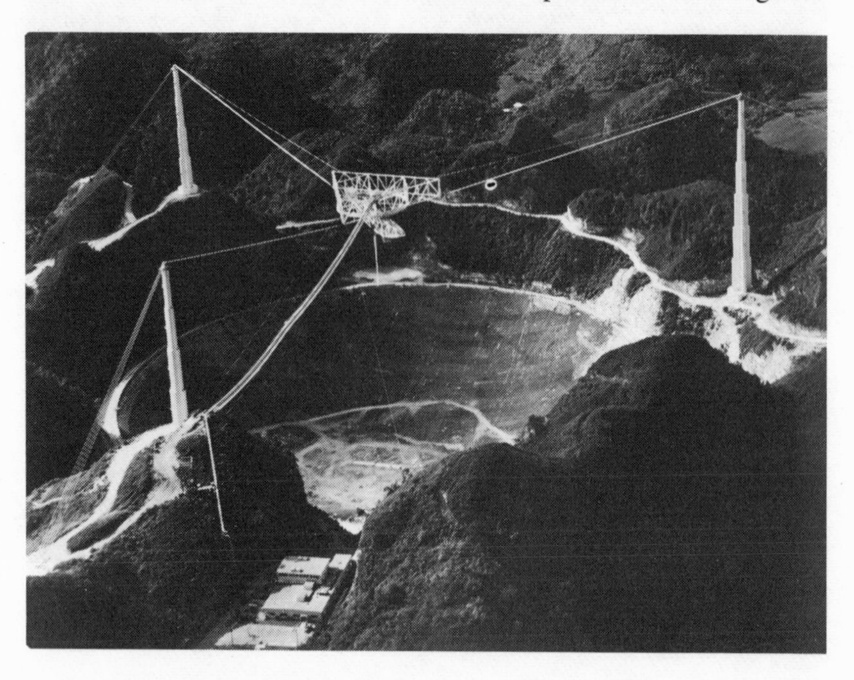

Fig. 5-2. The world's largest radio telescope, 1000 feet across, carved out of a hillside in Arecibo, Puerto Rico. (National Astronomy and Ionosphere Center, Cornell University)

in groups of two or more to get greatly improved resolving power. During the 1960s, the technique of *very long baseline interferometry* (VLBI) was worked out. Briefly, this technique uses 2 or more radio telescopes, separated by thousands of kilometers, but linked electronically so that they can work together. By working jointly, radio telescopes that were separated by half our globe have achieved resolving powers down to 0.01 second-of-arc.

The Sun as a Radio Star

Reber's original radio telescope was sensitive enough to track radio emissions from the heart of the galaxy, 10,000 parsecs away. Yet strangely, he could detect no radio signal from the Sun.

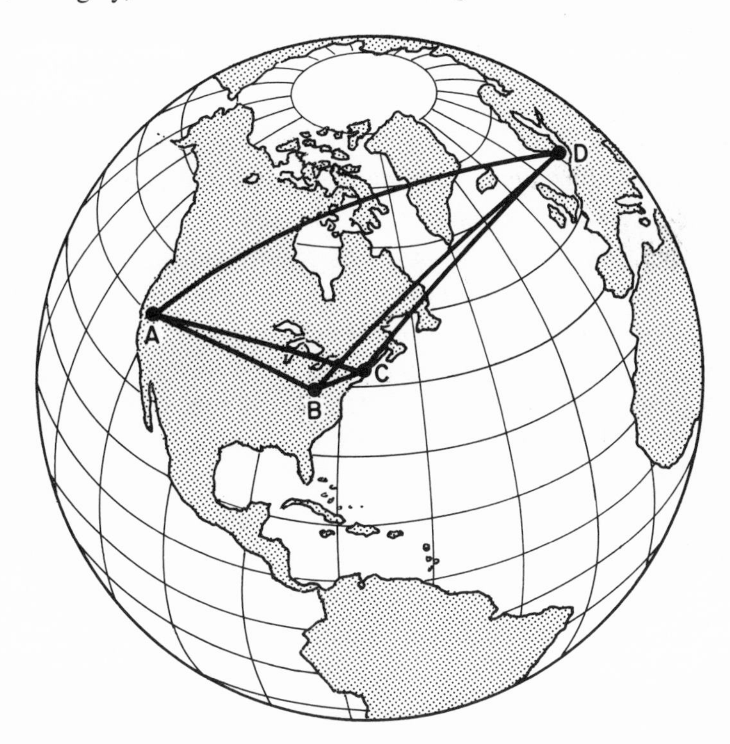

Fig. 5-3. In Very Long Baseline Interferometry (VLBI) several radio telescope facilities, separated by thousands of kilometers, are linked electronically to make cooperative observations.

In fact, it was not until World War II that anyone found radio emission from the Sun, and then the news was "hushed up" for 4 years.

On February 26, 1942, radar operators along the coast of England reported severe interference that made their radars practically useless. It was first feared that the source of the trouble was German jamming, but they quickly traced the interference to the Sun. Nothing like this had ever happened before, even though radars had been guarding the English coast against German planes since the very beginning of the war. Two days after it started the interference suddenly disappeared, and the radars functioned normally again.

Since the radars were vitally important to England's defense, the news about the mysterious interference from the Sun was kept secret. But in 1946, when the information was at last made public, astronomers quickly checked their records and found that a large sunspot had been crossing the center of the Sun's disc during those few days in 1942. It seemed obvious that the sunspot was associated with the 2 day long burst of radio energy from the Sun.

Sunspots had been known since Galileo's time. By the mid-20th century, astronomers had determined that the sunspots were linked to huge magnetic disturbances in the photosphere—the Sun's shining surface layer of plasma. Since plasmas can conduct electricity and support magnetic fields, it is not surprising that powerful radio signals can be generated from the Sun's plasma layers.

What *was* surprising was that most of the time the Sun was not a strong source of radio emission. Only during the upheavals called *solar flares,* which often accompany sunspots, does the Sun emit bursts of intense radio energy. Thus, radio astronomers and optical astronomers alike now speak of the "quiet" Sun or the "active" Sun. When the Sun is quiet it has few sunspots, and radio activity is at a minimum. When the sun is active there are many sunspots and solar flares, and correspondingly, much radio emission.

Radio astronomers have found that solar flares not only cause a burst of radio energy that may last for days; the flares also spew out vast clouds of electrons and protons that waft through space at speeds of better than 1000 kilometers per second. These clouds are invisible to optical telescopes.

In Chapter 7 we will see how these clouds of energetic particles affect the Earth.

Radio studies have also shown that the Sun's outermost layer of plasma—the corona—actually extends many millions of kilometers farther into space than the visible corona can be seen. And the corona's temperature is in excess of a million degrees Kelvin, much higher than the 6000°K temperature of the photosphere.

But although the corona plasma has a very high temperature, that does not mean it is very hot. The corona is practically a pure vacuum; its density is only 100 billionth of the density of the air we breathe. There is very little actual material in the corona. Individual

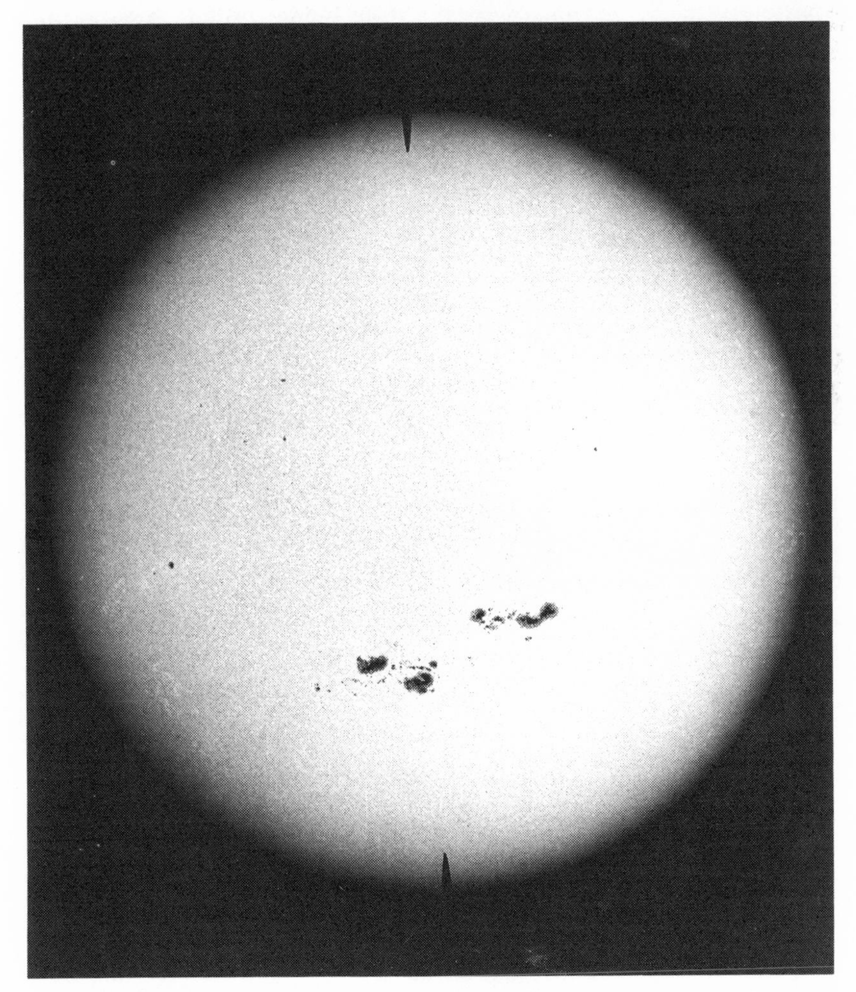

Fig. 5-4. The spotted Sun. The Sun is usually a quiet radio source, except when solar flares burst out from sunspot regions and emit intense radio energy. (Mt. Wilson and Palomar Observatories)

particles, protons and electrons, can be accelerated to very high speeds, and we measure such velocities as temperature. Temperature can be thought of as a measure of the energy invested in an average particle in the plasma. But heat is the total amount of energy in all the particles, and since there are so few particles in the corona, there is not much heat. You could freeze to death in this million degree plasma!

Although the high temperature of the corona is now accepted as an accurate measurement, the question of just how the coronal particles got all that energy is far from being settled. Possibly the strong magnetic fields of the Sun's photosphere somehow "pump" energy into the coronal particles.

In any case, these early radio observations of the Sun gave the first evidence that *non-thermal* energy processes are at work in the heavens.

Ordinarily thermal sources of energy radiate in a specific fashion. The higher the object's temperature, the shorter the wavelength at which it radiates. Thus, if you warm a metal bar moderately, it will not give off any visible light. Heat it enough, though, and it will glow —first dull red, then bright red, then white.

But even at white heat the metal is still giving off a fraction of its energy at longer wavelengths—including a tiny amount at radio wavelengths. All thermal sources of radiation behave this way: the higher their temperature, the shorter the wavelengths at which most of their radiation is emitted. But the longer wavelength radiation is still present. Thus the Sun, with a photosphere temperature of 6000°K, gives off most of its radiation in the wavelengths of visible light. Its radio emission from thermal sources is very low.

But when a solar flare erupts, a disproportionately large amount of radio energy bursts out. Obviously, something other than simple thermal emission is at work. Solar flares—and many other radio sources among the stars—have non-thermal energy sources driving them.

During the 1950s and 1960s, astronomers and physicists began to unravel the secrets of the Sun's non-thermal energy sources. They found powerful magnetic fields in sunspots, and this magnetic energy is released with explosive force when a solar flare takes place. Although the exact details are still far from being settled, it seems clear that the energy that causes solar flare radio bursts stems from these magnetic fields, rather than from simple thermal effects.

The Song of Hydrogen

When it comes to studying the structure of our Milky Way galaxy, radio astronomy arrived on the scene like the hero of a western movie, just in time to save the day. Or night.

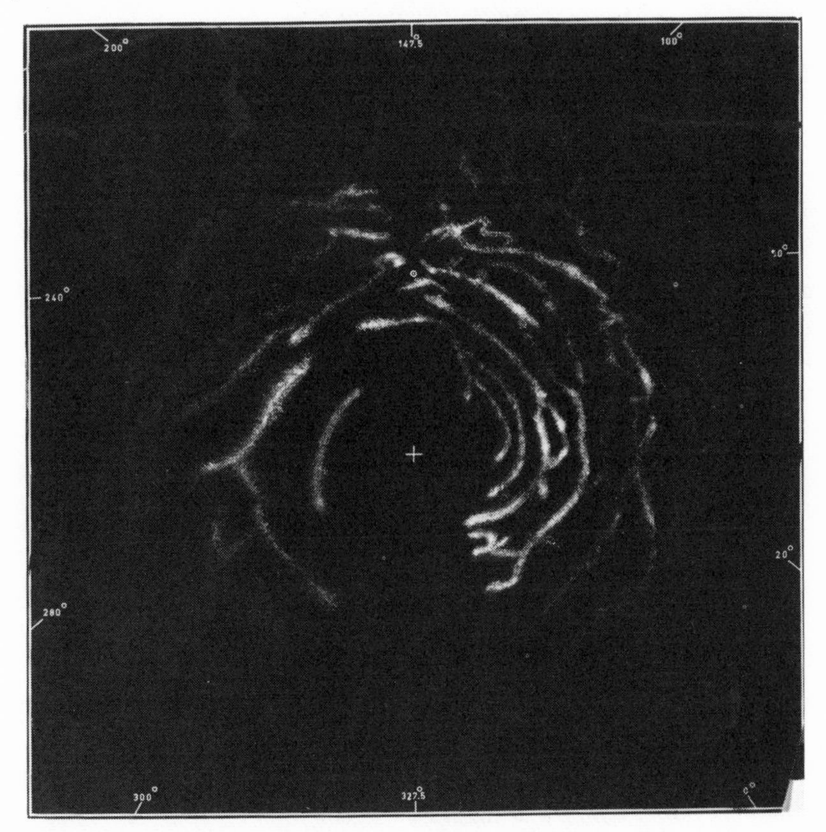

Fig. 5-5. Radio observations of the Milky Way, based on the 21-cm "song of hydrogen," penetrate the dust clouds and show the galaxy's spiral structure. (Leyden Observatory, Netherlands)

For generations, optical astronomers had tried to puzzle out the structure of the Milky Way. As you recall from Chapter 3, they found by 1930 that optical observations of the galaxy's heart are forever blocked by a curtain of interstellar dust.

But radio waves penetrate the interstellar dust quite easily.

Even though radio waves can theoretically get through the obscuring dust all the way from the center of the galaxy, are there any radio sources in the heart of the Milky Way that are strong enough to reach us? After all, the Sun is quiet most of the time. Radio astronomers searched in vain for "radio stars" for many years.

Meanwhile, back in 1944, the Dutch physicist H. C. Van der Hulst (born 1918) had predicted that hydrogen gas in intersteller space would emit a radio signal at a wavelength of 21 centimeters.

The hydrogen atom consists of a single proton and orbiting electron. Both the proton and electron are spinning on their axes, just as the Earth spins every 24 hours. The 2 particles might be spinning in the same direction—say, west to east—or they can be spinning in 2 different directions. Occasionally, in a hydrogen atom, where the 2 particles are spinning in the same direction, the electron will spontaneously "flip" and start spinning the other way. When this happens, the atom emits a pulse of radio energy at 21 centimeters wavelength.

This does not happen very often. For an individual hydrogen atom, the chances are that the atom will spend some 11 million years quietly before the electron flips and the radio pulse is emitted. And, of course, the strength of a radio pulse from a single hydrogen atom is minuscule.

But what the hydrogen atom lacks in quickness and strength it more than makes up for in numbers. There are enormous clouds of hydrogen out among the stars, so much neutral hydrogen gas that in 1951, when radio astronomers first "tuned in" on the 21 centimeter wavelength, they found a constant strong signal. They immediately dubbed it "the song of hydrogen."

At last astronomers could see beyond the clouds of obscuring interstellar dust and begin mapping out the structure of the Milky Way galaxy. They could not see individual stars, but the clouds of hydrogen gas outlined the spiral structure of the galaxy and confirmed the ideas of Shapley and his followers: the Milky Way is a spiral galaxy some 33,000 parsecs in diameter. And the Sun is tucked off to one side, in a spiral arm some 10,000 parsecs from the center of the galaxy.

Radio studies of the 21 centimeter emission have shown that hydrogen clouds are swirling outward from the core of the Milky Way galaxy and spinning out toward the rim of the galaxy's spiral. And there is a "halo" of very thin gas around the galaxy, giving off a weak but clear radio signal. It appears that hydrogen gas was somehow pushed outward from the center of the galaxy to form this halo.

Observations of other galaxies, such as our near twin M-31 in Andromeda, have shown that they also have weak "radio halos" surrounding them.

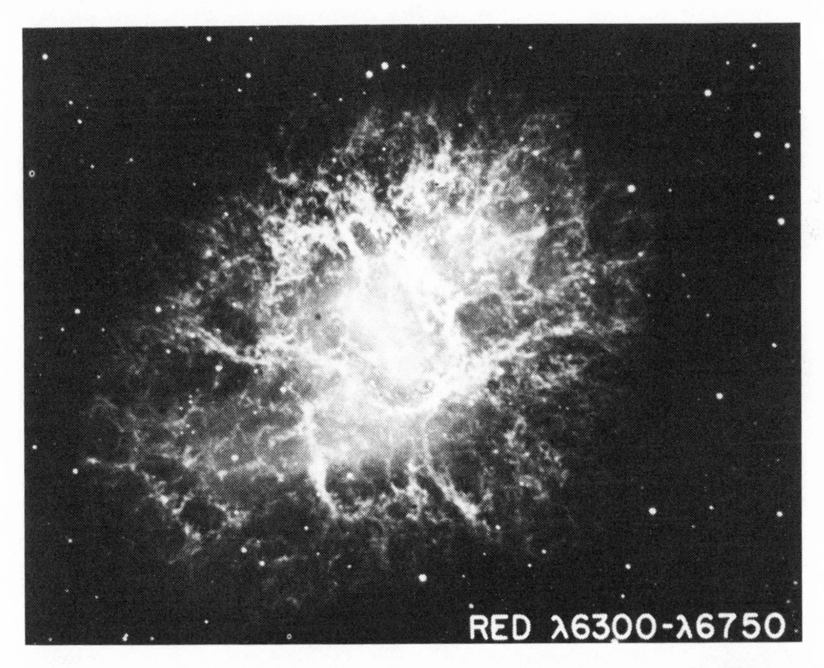

Fig. 5-6. The Crab Nebula, scene of a supernova explosion in 1054 AD, and still a gigantic "high energy physics laboratory" for astronomers. A pulsar at the center of the nebula provides the energy that keeps the wildly distorted plasma emitting radio, light, and x-ray energy. (Mt. Wilson and Palomar Observatories)

Discrete Sources

The 21 centimeter song of hydrogen was not the only radio signal coming from beyond the solar system.

Astronomers were on the lookout for "radio stars": that is, stars that are both bright enough to study optically and strong enough radio sources to study with radio telescopes. As is true in most endeavors, two ways of studying the same thing promised to unveil much more knowledge than either way could alone. The astronomers wanted to compare the behavior of a star in both the optical and radio wavelengths at once.

As soon as radio telescopes of sufficient sensitivity went into operation, in the late 1940's, astronomers began to pick up a number of pinpoint sources of radio energy. Although at first they thought they had found radio stars, they quickly saw that none of these sources

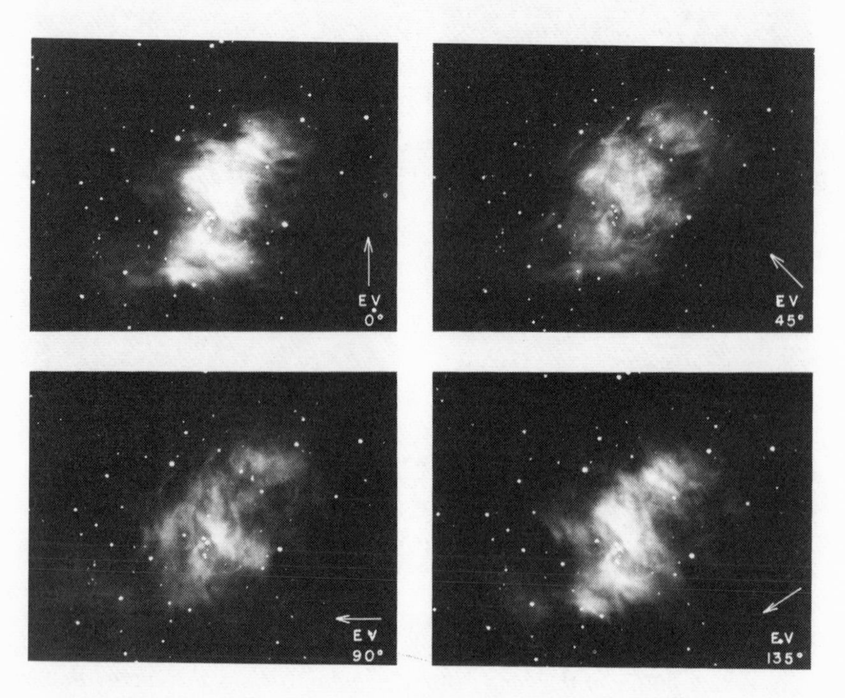

Fig. 5-7. The light from the Crab Nebula is heavily polarized, which leads astrophysicists to conclude that strong magnetic fields are present there. (Mt. Wilson and Palomar Observatories)

were stars at all. They are called *discrete sources,* meaning sources with definite locations in the sky, as distinguished from the broad radio emissions coming from the hydrogen clouds.

While no radio stars have been identified, despite several false leads, there are strong radio sources within the Milky Way that were once stars—stars that exploded.

One of the first and strongest of such discrete sources to be detected is in the constellation Taurus. Radio astronomers call it Taurus A—the strongest radio source in that constellation. Optical astronomers immediately recognized the location of Taurus A. It is in the famous Crab Nebula.

In the year 1054 (on July 4th!) Chinese and Japanese astronomers saw a new star suddenly appear in the sky, so bright that it could be seen in full daylight. They noted the appearance of the "guest star" in their records, and kept watch on it. After nearly 2 years it faded into invisibility.

Centuries later, European astronomers began to call these suddenly appearing and disappearing stars *novas,* after the Latin word for new. But while a nova seems to be a new star, it isn't. It is a star that has existed all along, then suddenly flared into a brilliance bright enough to be seen on Earth—the star has exploded. With telescopes, astronomers began to see many novas. They eventually learned that although a nova explosion is spectacular, it is not necessarily fatal to the star. Some stars puff off nova-type explosions year after year, like huffing steam engines. Of course, if a planet happens to be circling a star that goes nova, the planet may suddenly be wiped clean of atmosphere, oceans and life.

The explosion that created the Crab Nebula was no mere nova, however. Once optical telescopes came into use, astronomers found that there was a fuzzy patch of brightness in the constellation Taurus. Astronomers call anything that's shapeless and fuzzy a *nebula,* meaning cloud-like. When telescopes had improved to the point where the shape of the Taurus nebula could be seen clearly, it was dubbed the Crab Nebula.

By the end of the 19th century, European and American astronomers had rediscovered the original Chinese and Japanese records of the "guest star" and identified it with the Crab Nebula. By

1921, photographs of the Crab taken more than 10 years apart showed that the Nebula was expanding. The glowing plasma of the Crab is still rushing outward at speeds of better than 1000 kilometers per second. Astronomers decided that the Crab Nebula was a *supernova*—the remnant of a stellar explosion that destroyed a star.

When radio astronomers showed that the Crab was a strong radio source, the obvious question was: What is producing the radio emission?

It was soon determined that the Crab Nebula's radio emission was non-thermal, much like the radio bursts from the Sun. That is, the radio energy was not coming simply from heat energy. The radio emission was too intense to have simply a thermal source. The Russian astrophysicist I. I. Shklovsky (born 1916) suggested that the radio energy was coming from free electrons in the plasma that were accelerated to speeds close to the speed of light. The electrons were accelerated by strong magnetic fields in the plasma. This type of effect had earlier been noticed in nuclear physics laboratories, in a class of "atom smashing" accelerator called a *synchrotron*. Synchrotrons are designed to accelerate particles to near lightspeed by using magnetic fields.

A simple test could tell if synchrotron effects were present in the Crab Nebula. The strong magnetic fields that are needed for synchrotron effects would *polarize* the light coming from the Crab Nebula. When light is polarized, the light waves are all lined up more or less in a single plane—exactly vertical to your line-of-sight, say—rather than arranged randomly. A polarizing filter will dim out all the light waves except those along one plane.

When astronomers looked at the Crab Nebula through polarizing filters, they found that light was indeed heavily polarized. Shklovsky's synchrotron theory is now accepted as the best explanation of how the Crab Nebula—and many other discrete radio sources—produce radio energy.

Then another question arose. How could the Crab still be emitting so much energy after nearly 1000 years? Presumably the supernova explosion seen in 1054 demolished the original star. But the Nebula is still bright with visible light, and a strong radio source as well. As we will see in the next chapter, the Crab is also emitting a considerable amount of energy at other wavelengths, too.

Where does all this energy come from? There have been other supernovas in the Milky Way, both before and since the explosion in 1054. None of them has left such a brilliant beacon in the sky.

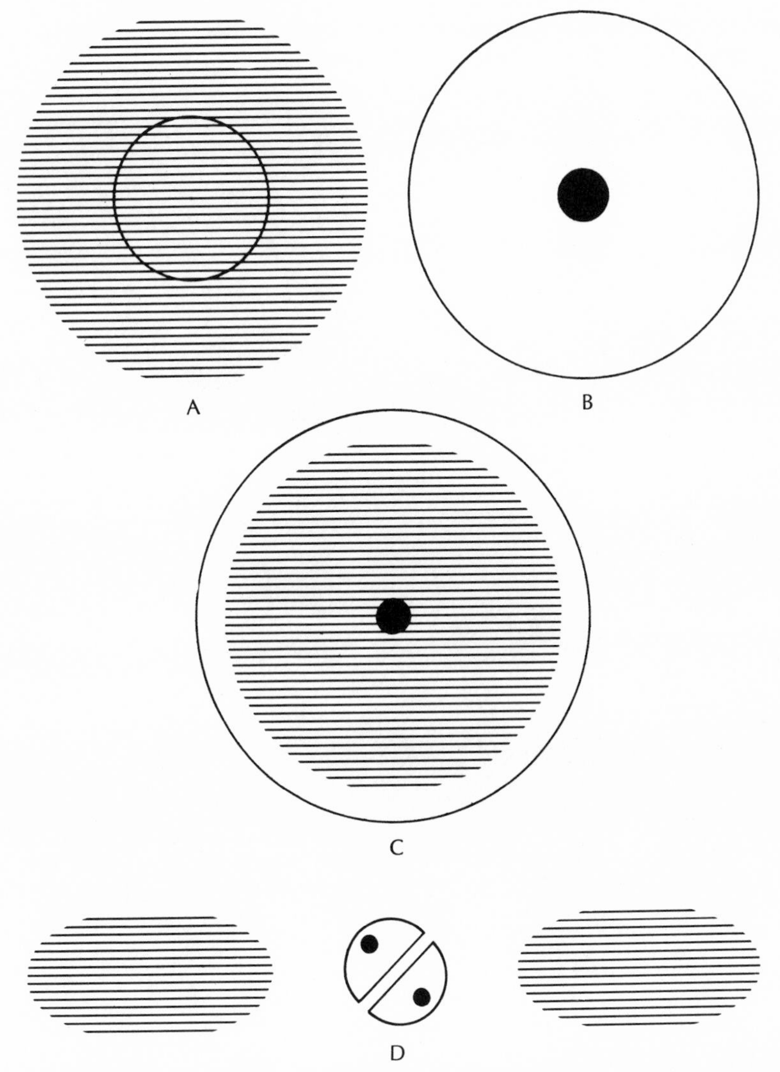

Fig. 5-8. Various types of radio galaxies. Drawing A shows a normal galaxy such as the Milky Way, as seen from above its north pole. The shaded area shows the region of radio emission. B is a "core emission" type of galaxy, and C has intense core emission plus an extended region of less-intense radio activity, as have been observed in the elliptical galaxy M 87. D is a double source, such as Cygnus A. (After Heeschen)

What powers the Crab Nebula? This question stayed unanswered until 1967. We will leave it unanswered until later in this chapter.

As radio telescopes got bigger and more powerful, radio astronomers started picking up thousands of discrete sources, all over the sky.

Fig. 5-9. The Cygnus A radio source, as seen by the 200-inch Hale telescope. (Mt. Wilson and Palomar Observatories)

A few of these sources obviously came from within the Milky Way, such as the Crab Nebula. But most of the discrete sources seemed to be much farther away: from other galaxies, in fact.

Most galaxies are not especially powerful emitters. The Milky Way, for example, puts out about 10^{28} kilowatts of radio energy. While that is 10 thousand billion kilowatts, it is still only about a millionth of the visible light energy that the Milky Way emits. A galaxy of some 100 billion stars, such as our Milky Way, puts out about 10^{34} kilowatts of energy in the wavelengths of visible light.

There are galaxies that are much stronger radio emitters. Astronomers call them *radio galaxies,* a clear but unpoetic description. Many radio galaxies are a hundred times stronger in radio emission than the Milky Way; others are a thousand and even a million times more powerful.

There are two types of radio galaxies. The first is "bright" (in radio wavelengths) mainly at the galaxy's core. The radio intensity of such "core emission" galaxies may range from a hundred to several thousand times that of normal galaxies.

The giant elliptical galaxy, M-87, is one of the largest and optically brightest galaxies known. To radio astronomers it is Virgo A, the strongest radio source in the constellation Virgo. Long exposure photographs of M-87 show a huge, nearly circular galaxy surrounded by a convoy of faint globular clusters.

When radio astronomers found unusually strong signals coming from the core of Virgo A, optical astronomers took short exposure photographs of the core to see if there was some detail visible that the long exposure photos had washed out. Sure enough, they found an intensely bright core. And streaking off to one side of it, a jet of glowing plasma!

Nothing like this had ever been seen before. The jet is 10,000 parsecs long. Both the central core and jet are bluish in color, and their light is highly polarized, much as the light from the Crab Nebula. This means that the radio emission from M-87 is also due to synchrotron radiation.

The second type of radio galaxy has two bright regions off to either side of the visible galaxy. Instead of being associated with the galaxy's core, these "double" sources seem to come from empty space!

The regions from which the radio signals emanate must be filled with a thin gas or plasma, but the material is invisible to optical telescopes.

The strongest radio source in the sky is Cygnus A. It not only has this double source outside its visible body, but Cygnus A also has two distinct radio sources at its core. Optically, Cygnus A looks very peculiar—like two galaxies colliding, or perhaps one galaxy splitting apart. Its radio output is about 1 million times stronger than that of a normal galaxy.

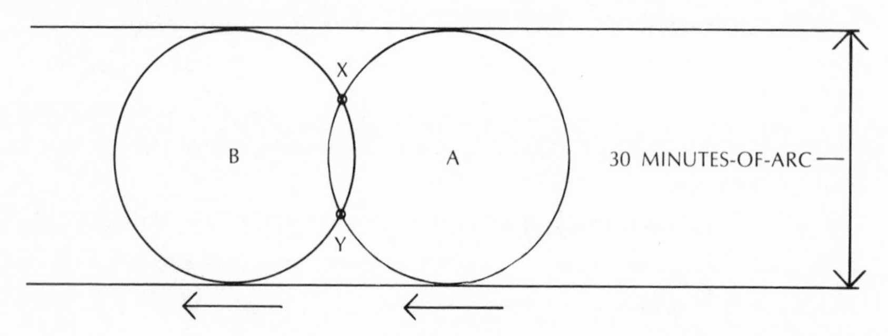

Fig. 5-10. The lunar occultation technique for pinpointing location of radio sources. Radio source disappears when the Moon covers it (position A) and reappears when the Moon moves away (B). Radio source must be at either point X or Y. A later measurement, when the Moon is in a slightly different position, shows which point is correct location of the radio source.

The double sources may also be due to synchrotron radiation; at least their radio emissions increase in intensity as the wavelengths get longer. Ordinary thermal sources give just the opposite behavior: the more intense radiation comes from the shorter wavelengths.

The discovery of such powerful radio emissions in galaxies caused a shock wave through the fields of astronomy and cosmology. How do galaxies produce this energy? In the case of the strong radio galaxies, there must be more energy produced in the galaxy than any existing theory can account for. What causes strange things such as the jet in M-87? And the invisible double sources?

It begins to look as if something violent happens in the cores of some galaxies, something that blows huge jets and clouds of plasma outward—something like an explosion!

Working together, radio and optical astronomers have discovered a regular hierarchy of celestial violence: solar flares, novas, supernovas, and even exploding galaxies. Each of them is associated with non-thermal energy sources that give off strong radio emissions.

To show this escalating scale of explosive violence, consider the Sun as a source of energy. The Sun steadily beams out a total of 3.8×10^{23} kilowatts of energy per second. That's 380 thousand billion billion kilowatts, mostly visible sunshine, each second.

A typical solar flare bursts out with some 10^{23} kilowatts of energy. This represents less than a second's worth of the Sun's total energy production. A nova, however, is equivalent in energy release to roughly 1000 years of solar output. A supernova releases as much energy in its first 24 hours as the Sun produces in a billion years!

When a galaxy explodes, as several have been observed to do, it takes the energy equivalent of some 20,000 supernova explosions. Just what titanic sources of energy can produce galactic explosions is completely unknown, as is the source of energy for the less spectacular but still impressive radio galaxies.

The Quasars

In December 1960, Thomas Mathews (born 1919) of the California Institute of Technology Radio Observatory and Allan R. Sandage (born 1926) of the Mt. Wilson and Palomar Observatories, found that the radio source 3C-48 is in the same position as a faint bluish star. (The term 3C-48 simply means that this radio source was the forty-eighth listed in the Third Cambridge Catalogue of radio sources.)

It certainly looked as if a radio star had been located at last. One major factor behind the discovery was that radio telescopes had by that time achieved sufficiently good resolving power so that they could narrow down the locations of radio sources to quite small angular dimensions in the sky, areas small enough so that only one star, or at most a few stars, could possibly be the radio source. Rather quickly after the announcement by Mathews and Sandage, several other faint blue "stars" were found to be radio sources.

Meanwhile early in 1963 a group of Australian radio astronomers pulled off a beautifully elegant experiment to pinpoint the location of some of the discrete radio sources. The Australians used the Moon as a tool to help them.

As the Moon moves in its orbit around the Earth, it passes in front

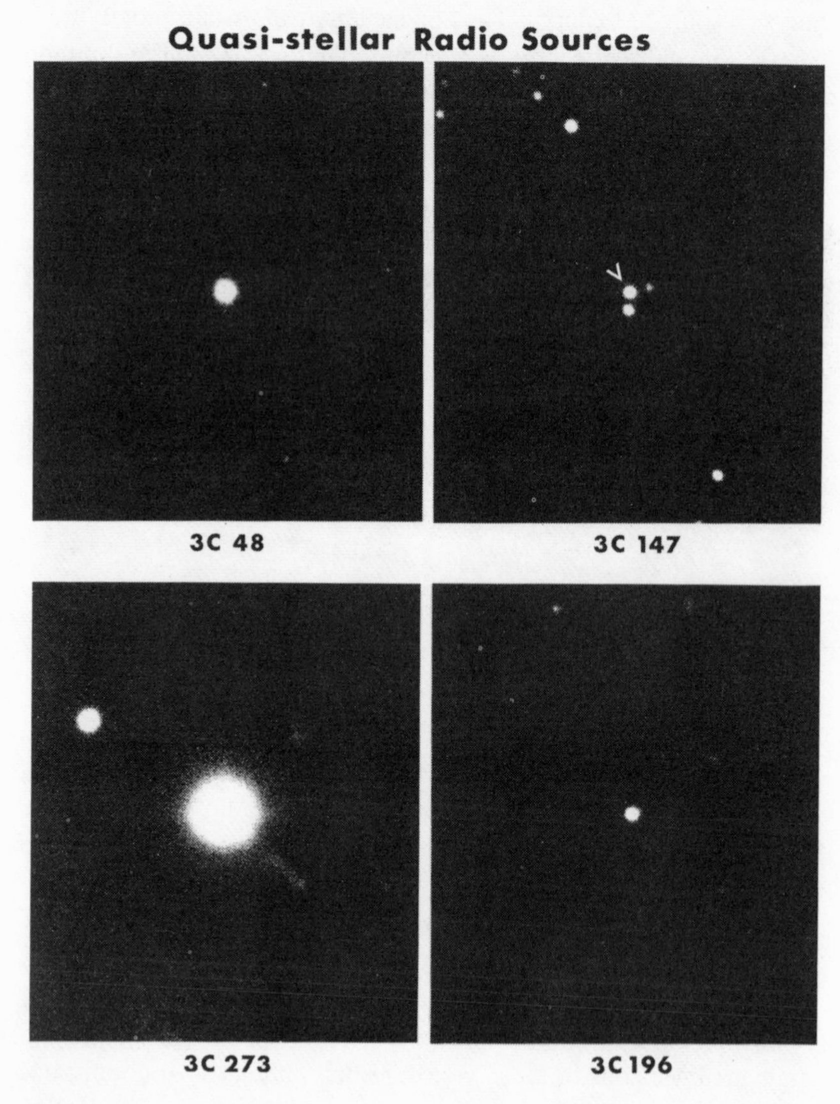

Fig. 5-11. Four quasars. The quasi-stellar objects have defied all attempts to explain them, so far. (Mt. Wilson and Palomar Observatories)

of stars and temporarily blocks them from our view. This is called *lunar occultation*. The Moon also occults discrete radio sources.

By timing when the radio source begins to fade out and how quickly its signal is completely blocked by the Moon, it is possible to determine how large the source is—that is, its angular size in seconds-of-arc. And since the Moon's location is known very accurately for every moment of its orbit, it is also possible to work out the precise location of the radio source.

One of the first radio sources the Australians looked at in this way was 3C-273. Surprisingly, it turned out to be two sources, not just one. Maarten Schmidt (born 1929) at Mt. Palomar quickly found that 3C-273 could be seen visually with a moderate sized telescope. In fact, it has shown up on routine astronomical photographs for years, and no one took it to be anything more than an ordinary faint blue star.

Now Schmidt turned the 200″ telescope on 3C-273 and found that it did indeed consist of two segments: a brilliant pinpoint of light and an elliptical tail. The tail is much dimmer than the pinpoint visually, but it gives off about 90% of the total radio energy coming from 3C-273.

By the end of 1963 it seemed clear that these radio stars were not stars at all. Astronomers began calling them "quasistellar objects": that is, something that is sort of like a star. Radio astronomers called them "quasistellar radio sources." In 1964 Hong-Yee Chiu (born 1932) of Columbia University coined the term *quasar,* a shorthand way of saying "quasi star."

The optical astronomers quickly began making spectroscopic studies of 3C-273 and other quasars. Their spectra were baffling. They did not match any of the spectra of known elements. Either the quasars were composed of chemical elements completely unknown on Earth, or they were made of ordinary elements under very unordinary conditions.

Schmidt suggested that the quasars are redshifted, and showed that the spectrum of 3C-273 turned out to be perfectly ordinary—except that all the spectral lines were shifted 16% toward the red. Quickly, astronomers began making redshift measurements of other quasars. The results were astounding.

The farthest known true galaxy is a radio galaxy called 3C-295. It shows a redshift of 46%, which means it is moving away from us at 36% of the speed of light. Its distance is estimated to be nearly 2 billion parsecs. Most of the quasars show much larger redshifts, and therefore are assumed to be hurtling away from us much faster,

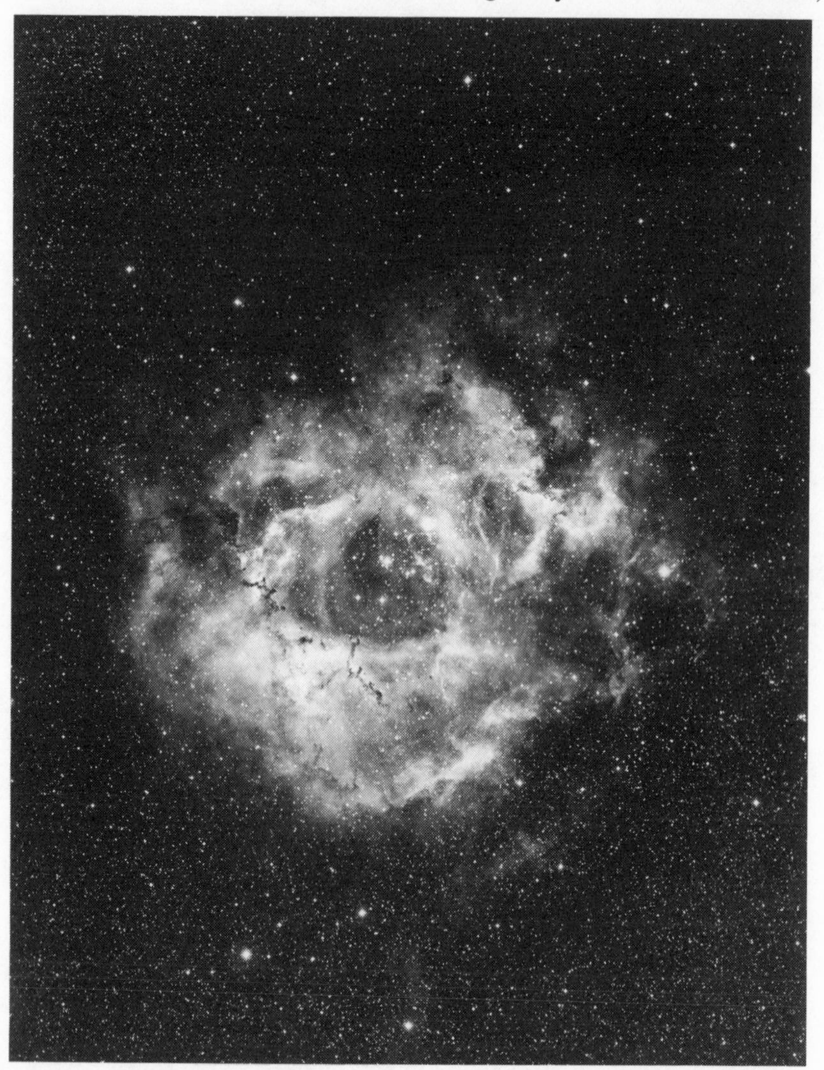

Fig. 5-12. In clouds of gas and dust such as the Rosette Nebula in Monoceros, protostars are evolving into new solar systems. Radio observations have shown that complex chemical compounds are present in such dark clouds. (Mt. Wilson and Palomar Observatories)

and thus must be much farther off. By 1971, several quasars had been found with redshifts so large that they must be travelling at nearly 90% of the speed of light. This means they must be nearly 5 billion parsecs away. The light that we see from them left those quasars more than 10 billion years ago, if all these assumptions are correct.

Most estimates for the age of the universe come out to somewhere around 10 billion years. Are we seeing, in the quasars, light that originated at the beginning of the universe?

But this is only the first part in the quasars' staggering series of surprises.

Having some idea of their distances, astronomers began to calculate how bright the quasars really are. The true energy output of any source can be determined from its apparent brightness and its distance. The calculations showed that the quasars must be far brighter than any galaxy. A typical quasar puts out 1000 times more visible light energy than the Milky Way galaxy. This means that a single quasar is shining with the ferocity of 100 trillion stars. And in the radio wavelengths, the quasars are among the strongest sources known, 1 million times stronger than the Milky Way.

Yet the quasars appear to be far smaller than any galaxy! Even at such tremedous distances, a galaxy-sized object would look like a fuzzy smudge. The quasars are tiny pinpoints of light, like single stars. How can so much energy be packed into such small objects? No one can answer.

And just to add an almost comical note, the quasars wink! Their brightnesses vary. They get brighter and dimmer, sometimes in a time as short as a day or even a few minutes. They are even "winking" at radio wavelengths.

The quasars are impossible in so many ways that some astronomers have questioned the assumption that they are "cosmologically" distant—that is, billions of parsecs away. If the quasars are "local," only a few million parsecs distant, then their light and radio outputs might be only 1/10,000 as much as previously estimated. But what produces the redshifts?

There are several possibilities. The quasars might be something like very huge stars, "superstars," some million times more massive than a star such as the sun. The redshift could be caused by simple gravitational drag on the light coming from such a superstar. Or, alternatively, the quasars might be clusters of stars—such as the massive globular clusters that "halo" our galaxy. In this view, the quasar star cluster has been hurled out of an exploding galaxy. The quasar redshifts are indeed caused by Doppler effects, because the quasars are moving like celestial shrapnel after being fired out of exploding galaxies. But the redshifts are *not* related to the expanding universe, nor are they indications of cosmological distances for the quasars.

At this time, none of these theories can be verified or disproved. We will take a longer look at the available evidence about the quasars, and the implications of the various theories about them, in Chapter 9.

Chemicals in Space

In 1936 radio astronomers at the Lincoln Laboratory of the Massachusetts Institute of Technology discovered that there are clouds of molecules in interstellar space. Rather quickly, radio telescopes all over the world began to tune in on the wavelengths where various types of molecules would be expected to radiate, and they found a number of different molecules, some of them rather complex.

This was a surprise. Hardly anyone expected to find molecules more complicated than H_2 in space, because it was believed that the strong ultraviolet radiation from very hot stars and other forms of hard radiation in space would break up any molecular combination and reduce it to simple atoms again.

Apparently the more complex chemicals are harbored in or near rather thick clouds of gas and dust, which screen them from the destructive radiation. Many astronomers feel that these chemicals are building up inside the clouds, and the clouds themselves represent the first stages of the formation of a new star and planetary system. We will see more of such *protostars* in the next chapter.

The first interstellar molecule to be found was the hydroxyl radical, OH. This is a molecule that does not remain stable under ordinary conditions on Earth. It is 2/3 of the common water molecule, H_2O.

The OH molecule was first detected near the radio source Cassiopeia A, because it absorbed a slight amount of the radio emission coming from that source. Since then, a number of molecules have been found both by absorption measurements and by emission: some molecular clouds emit a signal strong enough to be detected here.

Among the other molecules found in interstellar clouds are ammonia, water, and many compounds of hydrogen, carbon and sulfur. Such molecules perk up the interest of biochemists: these are the types of chemicals that go into the making of living organisms. It would seem that when new stars are being built all the basic ingredients for life are among the building blocks!

There is also an unidentified chemical, which the radio astronomers have dubbed x-ogen. No one seriously believes that it is a totally

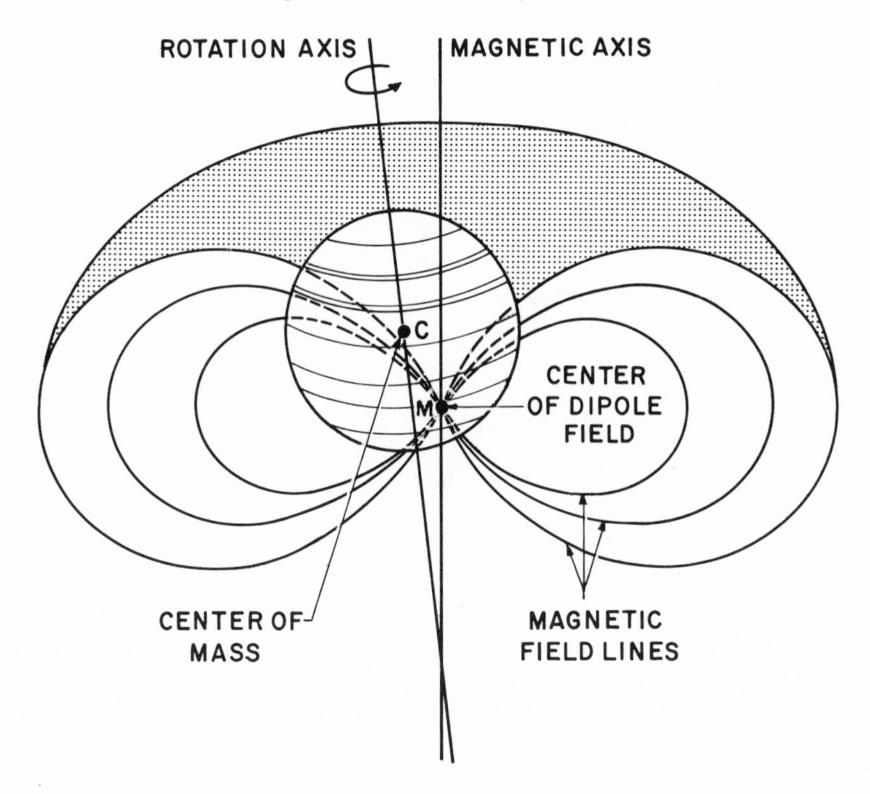

Fig. 5-13. Radio observations of the planet Jupiter indicate that the giant planet is surrounded by an extensive region of very energetic radio emission, similar to Earth's Van Allen radiation belts.

new element or compound; it is probably composed of ordinary atoms under very unEarthly conditions.

When the OH molecules were first discovered, there was also another set of wavelengths found for which no Earthly element or compound could be matched. It was called "mysterium" for a while. Further research led to the conclusion that mysterium was actually OH—but OH that had been excited to an energy level that is equivalent to a temperature of 10 trillion degrees!

This is not a measurement of the heat content of the OH molecules, but rather a measure of their energy level. The molecules are emitting radiation much in the way that a *maser* does. ("Maser" is an acronym for Microwave Amplification by Stimulated Emission of Radiation.) The maser was a forerunner of the laser. In a maser, molecules are excited by "pumping" energy into them. Then the molecules emit a much stronger radio signal than they could possibly do otherwise. Some of the OH molecules in the interstellar clouds may be doing just that, although how the energy is pumped into them is not yet known.

OH molecules have been detected in other galaxies, as well, showing that the forces at work in building protostars (and life?) are not confined to the Milky Way alone.

Radio Waves from the Planets

While radio astronomy was causing several furors in stellar astronomy, it also brought some startling surprises to the study of the solar system.

You recall that ordinary thermal sources of radiation put out their most intense energy at the shorter wavelengths. Thus the Sun is much stronger in visible light than radio output, unless some nonthermal event such as a solar flare suddenly erupts with a burst of strong radio noise.

The planets do not emit light of their own. They reflect sunlight. They also absorb some of the energy they receive from the Sun and then reradiate it at other wavelengths. For example, our own Earth absorbs visible and infrared energy from the Sun and reradiates it as longer wavelength infrared energy, for the most part. This is the principle behind the use of greenhouses.

Most of the electromagnetic radiation we receive from the planets is simply reflected sunlight. But there is some infrared radiation reradiated by the planets, and an even smaller amount of radio energy. The intensity of this reradiated energy is a measure of the temperature of the body from which it comes. Thus radio measurements can be used to determine a planet's temperature, just like optical or infrared measurements.

When radio astronomers turned their antennae toward the planets, one of the first surprises they received was that the temperature of Venus seemed to be at least 600°K (640°F), hot enough to boil water three times over!

No astronomer had been prepared for this result. True, Venus is closer to the sun than Earth: its distance is 0.7 AU. But the planet is completely covered with bright white clouds, which reflect most of the solar energy coming in. In fact, these clouds are so thick that no one has ever seen the surface of Venus. If the surface could be seen, ordinary measurements of its temperature could have been made long ago.

Infrared measurements of Venus' temperature *had been* made many times in earlier years. They showed temperatures ranging from 235 to 285°K (-40 to -50°F). This is about what theory predicted for the temperature of the cloud tops.

But the infrared measurements could not penetrate the perpetual cloud cover and get down to the surface. The radio measurements could. Although only a small amount of the planet's output of energy comes out in radio wavelengths, there is enough radio emission coming from Venus to allow radio astronomers to judge its temperature by the intensity of the radio emissions. And the longer the radio wavelengths used, the hotter the temperature reading is, since the longer wavelengths appear to come from deeper inside the atmosphere. Measurements made in the 3 to 21 centimeter range of the microwave spectrum returned readings of 600 to 700°K: the longest wavelength measurements came from close to the surface.

How could this be? Some astronomers suggested that Venus was a supergreenhouse, where virtually all the solar energy that gets through the clouds is trapped very efficiently by the atmosphere.

In a terrestrial greenhouse, the glass walls allow sunlight in but block the longer wavelength infrared that is reradiated by the plants and soil. This energy is held inside the greenhouse and raises its interior temperature. Our own atmosphere displays a greenhouse effect: carbon dioxide and water vapor molecules in our atmosphere absorb much of the infrared energy reradiated by our planet's surface, thereby raising the atmosphere's temperature.

Venus must have a fantastic greenhouse effect in its atmosphere, these astronomers reasoned. It had already been postulated that Venus' atmosphere was rich in carbon dioxide, and traces of water vapor had been seen in the clouds.

Fig. 5-14. Jupiter, showing its Red Spot and Ganeymede, one of its 12 moons. (Mt. Wilson and Palomar Observatories)

But others could not believe that this was a true picture of the surface of Venus. They suggested that the radio measurements were actually coming from energetic electrified particles high in Venus' atmosphere—an ionosphere similar to the ionosphere of Earth that reflects long wavelength radio broadcasts across continents and oceans.

This "hot ionosphere" model of Venus conflicted with the "hot surface" model. It was not until the flight of the Mariner 2 spacecraft in 1962 that the argument was resolved. The Mariner measurements showed that Venus' surface actually is more than 700°K. More on the Mariner and Russian Venus spacecraft flights in Chapter 7.

Meanwhile, radio astronomers did find a "hot ionosphere" of sorts. Not on Venus. On Jupiter.

The solar system's largest planet is also the most active in radio signals. At wavelengths of 3 to 100 centimeters, Jupiter is radiating

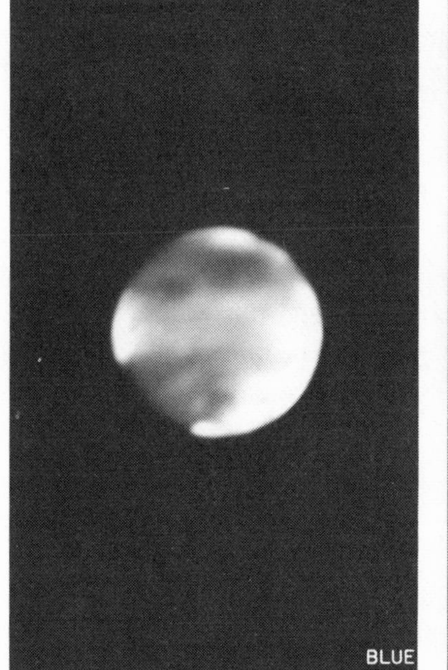

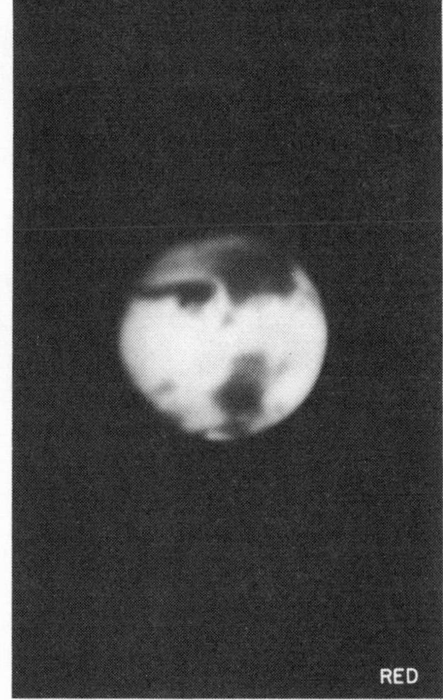

Fig. 5-15. Two views of the planet Mars. Note that the polar caps show up best in blue light, while the "oases" are much more visible in red light. (Mt. Wilson and Palomar Observatories)

strongly. It is the strongest radio source in the sky, in fact, except for the Sun during a solar flare period. (The radio sources outside the solar system are inherently millions of times stronger, of course, but the actual radio energy we receive from them is tremendously diminished by their distances.)

The steady radio emission coming from Jupiter corresponds to a temperature of more than 25,000°K. However, no one has suggested that this is the actual temperature of the planet. Jupiter's temperature has been reliably measured by other means, and it is more like 130°K at the highest—more than 100° below zero on the Fahrenheit scale.

The radio energy is apparently coming from very energetic particles suspended above Jupiter's visible body. These particles must be trapped by the planet's magnetic field, much as Earth's magnetic field has trapped the particles that make up the Van Allen belts. (The Van Allen radiation belts around Earth will be discussed in more detail in Chapter 7.) For now, the important point is that radio observations of Jupiter provide evidence for a Jovian magnetic field. As we will see, neither the Moon, Venus, nor Mars has a significant field around it.

While the radiation belt type of radio noise is constant, there are also strong bursts of radio energy coming from Jupiter at a wavelength of about 15 meters. These bursts come in scattered clusters. An individual burst can be anywhere from 1/1000 of a second to 10 to 30 seconds long. And a series of bursts will rattle off within a few minutes of each other, and then all will be quiet again. To many radio astronomers, it almost sounds like the kind of radio noise made by lightning storms on Earth.

But it is much more powerful. The energy in these bursts is something like the energy released by a 1 megaton hydrogen bomb—for every second of the burst!

Stranger still, the bursts seem to be controlled to some degree by the position of Jupiter's closest large moon: Io. When Io is in a direct line between Jupiter and the sun, the bursts are 5 times weaker than when Io is 90° off the Sun-Jupiter line.

Why should this be? No one knows. It seems certain the Jupiter's magnetic field—and the trapped high energy particles—extend out far enough so that Io orbits within them. And this field is about 1000 times stronger than Earth's magnetic field.

Is Io acting like the tuning crystal in a radio as it orbits through Jupiter's powerful magnetic field? It is possible. Is there something being beamed in from the Sun that enhances the radio bursts on Jupiter, and is blocked by Io when the moon gets between Jupiter and the Sun? Again all we can say is: possibly. No one knows what causes the radio bursts, and no one will know until spacecraft get close enough to the giant of the planets to make investigations that are much more detailed than any we can conduct from Earth.

The most recent surprise to come from radio studies of the planets deals with Mars.

Once men thought Mars might be a planet much like our own, a

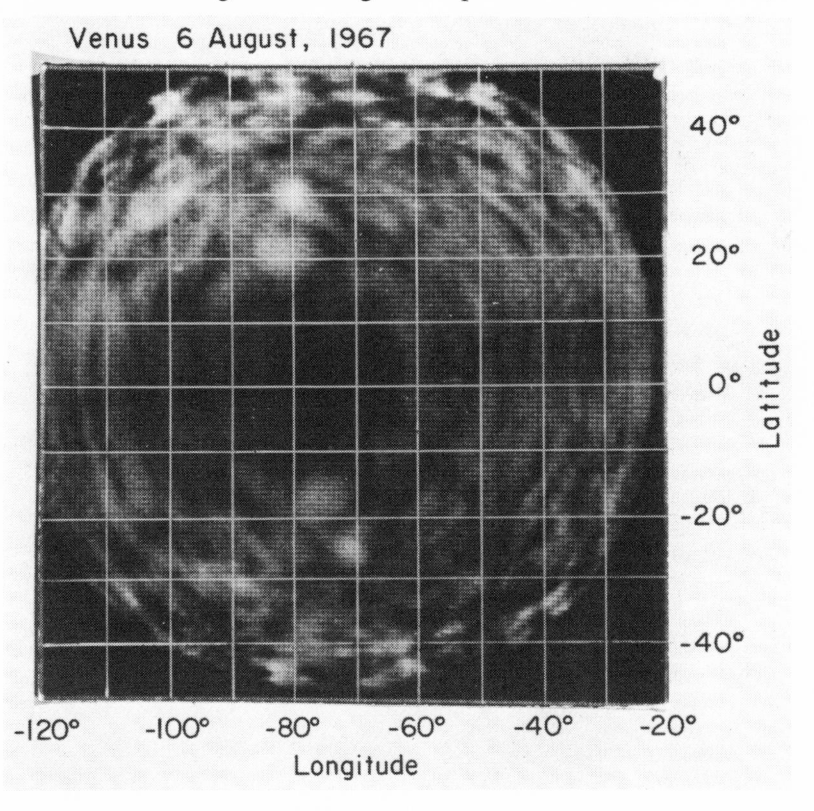

Fig. 5-16. A radar view of Venus. The brightest spots show possible mountain chains.

world where life might exist. But the more we learn about Mars, the worse it looks. It is a bitterly cold world, where temperatures plummet more than 100° below freezing every night, winter and summer. The average surface temperature of Mars is 235°K (room temperature is 70°F and 300° on the Kelvin scale). There is no liquid water on Mars' surface, although there are glistening white polar caps, apparently made of frozen carbon dioxide: "dry ice," not snow or water ice. The Martian atmosphere is so thin that even if it were made of pure oxygen it would be too thin for us to breathe. And it has no free oxygen in it; it is mostly carbon dioxide.

But recent radio studies of Mars' surface have shown that there might be liquid water in the top few centimeters of the soil.

The radio waves emanating from Mars' soil give a measure of the soil's temperature. The shortest wavelengths should give the highest temperature, since they presumably come from the surface. Longer wavelengths, which come from several centimeters below the surface, should give lower temperatures because the ground gets cooler beneath the sun heated surface.

But radio observations made at wavelengths of 1 millimeter to 20 centimeters have shown that the Martian soil temperature is higher at the longer wavelengths than theory had predicted. This has led Carl Sagan (born 1934) of Cornell University and others to suggest that there might be liquid water just beneath the surface, acting as a sort of heat trap, keeping the temperature of the soil higher than it would be if it were dry.

Sagan and his colleagues have gone so far as to produce laboratory models of soil with slight amounts of liquid water just below the surface, and have shown that microwave radiation from the model closely matches the observed radiation from Mars.

If there is liquid water in the Martian soil, then the chances for life on Mars might be very strong indeed. But this is a big, unconfirmed *if,* at the moment of this writing.

Radar Astronomy

Radio astronomers have not been content merely to search for signals from the sky. Ever since 1946, when radar pulses were first successfully bounced off the Moon by engineers in Hungary and the United States, astronomers have eagerly tried to use the technique of radar to learn more about the solar system.

The basic idea behind radar is to generate radio wavelength energy and send it out through an antenna to a target. The target reflects some of the energy back to the antenna. This reflected energy can then be analyzed to determine how far away the target is, its size and shape, how good an electrical conductor it is, et cetera. Radar was first developed in England just before the outbreak of World War II.

The biggest problem with probing the planets by radar is the sheer distance involved. Although radar returns were successfully obtained from the Moon in 1946, it was not until 1959 that a team at Massachusetts Institute of Technology's Lincoln Laboratory succeeded in getting a radar signal back from Venus. And no wonder. For the same outgoing energy, Venus returns a radar signal that is some 10 million times fainter than the Moon's! Larger, more powerful, more sophisticated radars were needed to reach the planets. Even so, it took the MIT engineers and scientists several weeks to "sort out" the radar return from Venus from the background radio noise of the heavens.

Also in 1959, a group at Stanford University bounced radar signals off the Sun's corona. The ionized plasma of the Sun reflects certain wavelengths of radio energy just as the solid body of a planet would.

The first use of radar in astronomy, though, was to help detect meteoroids.

If you stand outside on any dark, clear night, you will soon see a few meteors streak across the sky. Millions of them flash into the Earth's atmosphere every 24 hours. Astronomers have for many years used wide angle cameras with their shutters left open all night to catch the meteors that are bright enough to make a visible trace across the sky. (A note on terminology: A *meteoroid* is the object itself; a *meteor* is the flash of light the object makes when it burns up in the atmosphere; and a *meteorite* is what—if anything—is left of the object after it reaches the ground.)

During World War II, radar operators often complained that

certain wavelengths were often swamped by signals that seemed to be coming from the sky. Astronomers soon realized that the radars were picking up meteoroids—millions of them, boring into our atmosphere every hour of the day and night.

Although several tons of meteoric debris sift through our atmosphere every day, most of the meteoroids that invade our air are no bigger than dust grains. They do not leave a luminous trail bright enough to be seen. And even large meteors cannot be seen when the sun is up. But radar picks up all the meteors easily, since even a speck of dust hitting our atmosphere at meteoroid speed (13 to 72 kilometers per second) ionizes the air in its wake and makes a perfect radar target.

Although studies of meteors and the Sun have been rewarding, radar astronomy has made its biggest impact in studies of the planets. As you might expect, these studies have concentrated on the planets closest to us: Venus, Mars, and Mercury.

Since the 1880s astronomers had agreed that the planet closest to the Sun, Mercury, went through its 88 day orbit in "locked" rotation. That is, its day was equal to its year, both of which were equal to 88 Earth days. They also agreed that Mercury always kept one side facing the Sun, and the other side turned away, just as our Moon is "locked" in its rotation around the Earth and always keeps the same face turned toward us.

Three generations of astronomers were dead wrong.

Radar measurements of Mercury made in 1965 by Gordon H. Pettengill (born 1926) and Rolf B. Dyce (born 1929), with the 300 meter "dish" in Arecibo, showed that Mercury spins on its axis in something like 59 days.

How can radar measure a planet's spin? The technique takes advantage of the Doppler effect. For a rotating body such as a planet, the side moving away from the radar antenna will return a slightly longer wavelength signal than the side moving toward the antenna. The faster the spin, the bigger the difference in wavelengths.

Making such measurements on Mercury required the most sensitive radar equipment. Many astronomers at first refused to believe the results. How could three generations of astronomers all have been wrong?

The answer was incredibly simple. Optical astronomers tend to observe Mercury once a year, when conditions are most favorable. Being so small and so close to the Sun, Mercury is a difficult planet to see. Each time the astronomers looked at Mercury they saw—faintly—pretty much the same features. Their conclusion was that the planet always had the same side facing the Sun *when they observed it*. From this valid conclusion they assumed that Mercury *always* has the same side facing the Sun: that all through its orbit it was in locked rotation.

The radar measurements showed that Mercury rotates not once in every orbit around the Sun, but 1-1/2 times. The optical astronomers had concluded that Mercury made 4 complete revolutions around its axis each Earthyear, since it made 4 orbits around the Sun each Earthyear. Actually, Mercury makes 6 revolutions around its axis for every 4 orbits around the sun.

After an initial period of argument, the optical and radar astronomers got together to measure Mercury's spin rate. The best value they have come up with is 58.65 Earth days, which indeed means that Mercury's spin is in "3/2 resonance:" that is, for every two orbits around the Sun it rotates on its axis 3 times.

What about Venus' spin rate? Venus is perpetually cloud covered, so we cannot see its surface and optically determine the length of its day. Guesses have ranged from 24 hours to 225 days, which is the length of Venus' year.

Radar has penetrated the clouds to show that Venus rotates very slowly: it spins once each 243 Earth days. Venus' "day" is longer than its year!

Not only that, but the planet rotates backwards! All other planets in the solar system spin from west to east, counterclockwise as seen from their north poles. But Venus lumbers along from east to west, clockwise. If the clouds were not obscuring the Sun, and there was anyone on Venus' surface to look, the Sun would rise in the west and set in the east.

And here is another oddity—Venus' rotation rate is such that the planet always shows the same side to Earth when our two worlds are at their closest approach. Does this mean that Earth's gravitational pull has affected the spin rate of our sister world?

Venus *is* our sister world, by the way, even though it is hardly like Earth under its clouds. We have already seen that radio observations of Venus indicate its surface temperature is something like a red hot oven. Still, Venus is almost the same size as Earth, and radar probes have shown that Venus apparently has continents and mountain chains somewhat similar to Earth's.

Pettengill and his colleagues have also used radar to map the topography of Mars. They find that there are differences in elevation of about 12 kilometers between the highest and lowest points measured. For comparison, the difference in elevation between the peak of Mt. Everest and the bottom of the Marianas Trench in the Pacific Ocean is roughly 20 kilometers. Radar studies of Mars have not given clear indications of mountain chains, such as have been found on Venus. Nor have the radar "maps" been able to match up the dark and light features seen on Mars with differences in elevation.

One of the most important uses of radar in astronomy is rather unspectacular: measuring the Astronomical Unit to the best accuracy possible. The AU is the basic yardstick of astronomy, and its accuracy helps to define the size of our solar system and even the distances to the stars. Radar measurements of the distance to Venus have been used to define the AU down to an accuracy of 1 part in 10 million. The AU can now be expressed in light seconds—499.004785. While such accuracy is vital in planning spacecraft missions to the planets and in measuring interstellar distances, we can be satisfied with a less precise value for the AU of 149,598,000 kilometers.

Ozma, Pulsars and Little Green Men

In 1959, with radio astronomy in full bloom all over the world, a pair of Cornell University physicists made a startling suggestion.

Giuseppi Cocconi (born 1914) and Philip Morrison (born 1915) pointed out that radio telescopes might be sensitive enough to pick up signals deliberately beamed out by other intelligent races, living on planets circling other stars.

Even a few years earlier such a suggestion would have been laughed at. But most astronomers were by then willing to admit that there could be life—even intelligent life—elsewhere in the universe. And Cocconi and Morrison were not only highly respected scientists, they were very persuasive arguers.

The next year Frank Drake (born 1930), director of the National Radio Astronomy Observatory at Green Bank, West Virginia, launched Project Ozma. The name came from the queen of the mythical land of Oz. Drake and his colleagues picked two stars for study: Tau Ceti and Epsilon Eridani. They were selected because they are stable, long lived stars, the type that could allow life enough time to evolve and develop intelligence (a feat that took nearly 5 billion years in this solar system). There was no evidence for planets circling either star, but that did not mean none were there. Both stars are between 3 and 4 parsecs distant: an Earth-like planet would be totally undetectable to us at that distance.

Between May and July of 1960, for a total of 150 hours, Drake allowed the 85′ radio telescope to listen for signals of intelligent life from the two stars, on the 21 centimeter wavelength. Nothing was heard except completely natural radio emissions.

No one was daunted by the lack of success. For one thing, it would have been truly staggering if the first stars picked to be monitored did harbor intelligent life. Then again, only 150 hours could be squeezed from the busy radio telescope's schedule. Finally, unless the inhabitants of the target planetary systems were deliberately beaming signals toward us, the radio telescope probably could not have picked up anything. (And, of course, there may have been intelligent signals received, but not recognized. After all, alien beings might use wavelengths or types of signals that we cannot understand.)

So astronomers concluded that they would have to wait for much more powerful and sensitive radio equipment before they could hope to make contact with another intelligent race.

Then, in the summer of 1967, Antony Hewish (born 1924) of

Cambridge University and a graduate student of his, Jocelyn Bell, picked up a strange, pulsed radio signal.

Nothing like this had ever been detected before. The radio signals came in millisecond pulses, bursts that were only 10/1000 to 20/1000 of a second long and came every 1.33730113 seconds. The precise timing of the pulses was as accurate as could have been made by any chronometer on Earth!

The precision of the pulses tempted astronomers to wonder if these signals were coming from an intelligent civilization. For a few weeks, they debated the "LGM (Little Green Men) Theory" as one way of explaining the pulses.

The Cambridge group and other radio astronomy teams soon found many other pulsed radio sources in the sky. They were dubbed "pulsars."

By the end of 1967, Thomas Gold (born 1920) of Cornell University and several other theoreticians had proposed completely natural explanations for the pulsars. The LGM theory was put to rest, but the "natural" explanations for the pulsars are only slightly less fantastic than little green men. Gold's explanation predicted a pulsar in the heart of the Crab Nebula.

When radio telescopes of the proper wavelength were turned to the Crab, they found the pulsar! Not only that, but the Crab Nebula pulsar has even been photographed, winking on and off 30 times per second.

The pulsar is an incredibly dense, fast spinning neutron star, the collapsed core of the original star that suffered the supernova explosion. There is still a huge amount of energy invested in the collapsed remains of the star, and this energy is what we detect as light, radio waves, and higher energy radiation. Thus one of the original questions raised by radio astronomy—the energy source of the Crab Nebula—has been answered by radio astronomy. The supernova explosion did not totally destroy the original star; a tiny pulsar remains to provide the driving power that keeps the Crab alight. We will go into more detail about the pulsars further on.

Little Green Men or not, astronomers are still thinking about the possibilities of life elsewhere in the cosmos.

In the summer of 1971, a team of engineers and scientists of many disciplines met for an 11 week study at the National Aeronautics and Space Agency's Ames Research Center, near San Francisco. They called their summer study Project Cyclops, and its aim was to examine the possibilities of finding extraterrestrial life.

One of their conclusions was that an array of some 1000 radio telescopes, interconnected and spread over a distance of some 15 kilometers, could detect deliberately beamed signals from as far as 1000 lightyears away. Such a radio telescope array might even be able to pick up the ordinary radio broadcasts from a nearby planetary system, the everyday radio "traffic" such as that which constantly flickers around our own planet.

The cost of such a complex array of radio telescopes would be —well, astronomical. But the interesting point is that radio technology has become powerful enough to allow us to consider now the prospects of reaching out 1000 lightyears in our quest for other intelligent races.

6.

New Eyes

While the radio astronomers were exploring the heavens through their atmospheric window, other men and women were developing different types of instruments that operate at different wavelengths.

These new "eyes" for astronomers include infrared telescopes, ultraviolet, x-ray and gamma ray receivers, and even neutrino detectors, which are placed in mile deep mines to study the sun!

Infrared Astronomy

The roots of infrared astronomy go back to 1800, when William Herschel (the discoverer of Uranus) first realized that there was an invisible form of energy beyond the red end of the optical spectrum that conveys heat. In a famous experiment, he broke up white light coming from the sun into a rainbow-like spectrum by passing it through a glass prism. Thermometers placed at each color of the visible spectrum all read about the same temperature. But a thermometer placed in the seemingly unlit area beyond the red end of the spectrum registered a much higher temperature than any of the others.

Clearly, there was an invisible form of radiation carrying considerable heat energy. Herschel dubbed it *infrared* radiation. We use it today in heat lamps, and indeed, it is the infrared radiation from a fireplace that heats a room.

The infrared portion of the electromagnetic spectrum begins where the visible region ends, at 0.75 micron (a micron is a millionth of a meter, and equal to 10,000 angstroms). The IR part of the spectrum ends at 3000 microns, which is equal to 3 millimeters. Beyond this point is the microwave region.

Not all of this infrared region is accessible to ground based astronomers. There are many absorption bands in the Earth's atmosphere, due to water vapor, carbon dioxide, and other molecules that block out parts of the infrared wavelengths before they can reach the surface. Most of the astronomical work that has been done in the IR has been in the 0.75 to 22 micron region.

The region between 0.75 and 1.2 microns is called the *photographic infrared,* because photographic film can be exposed by these wavelengths. The first photograph in the IR was made by John Herschel (1792-1871), William's son, in 1840. He photographed the sun in infrared.

Between 1.2 and 5.2 microns is the *near infrared.* Atmospheric transmission shuts down from 5.2 to 8 microns making that region useless. From 8.2 to 22 microns is the *long wavelength infrared* region. However, there are absorption bands in this region, especially between 14 and 17 microns, so the entire region is not accessible.

For about a century, astronomers have used simple IR detectors such as the *thermocouple* to measure the temperatures of the planets and stars. The thermocouple is little more than two strips of different metals joined together. When IR radiation heats the junction between the two, it generates a tiny electrical current. By measuring the current you can determine the intensity of the radiation and, working backwards, the temperature of the source planet or star that the telescope is aimed at.

Much more sophisticated IR detectors have been developed since

World War II. Among these are very sensitive *bolometers.* A bolometer uses a blackened metal foil to absorb infrared energy. As the foil heats up, its electrical resistance increases. By measuring the change in electrical resistance, you can calculate the amount of IR energy striking the foil. The first bolometers were used as early as 1880. But by 1960, bolometers had become sensitive enough to measure the minuscule amounts of 8 to 14 micron radiation coming from Saturn.

The most sensitive IR detectors use semiconducting crystals—something like transistors. These are known as *photoconductive* de-

Fig. 6-1. The Moon, showing the large crater Tycho near the south pole, where high infrared radiation has been detected. (Mt. Wilson and Palomar Observatories)

tectors. Like optical photocells, the photoconductive detectors can release a flow of electrical current when a single photon of the proper wavelength strikes them.

Until the advent of radio astronomy, all the temperature measurements of the planets were made in the IR. And except for unusual cases such as Venus, these measurements have been quite reliable.

Infrared "mapping" of the Moon has shown that some lunar areas are warmer than others. The prominent crater Tycho, near the lunar south pole, is an example of this. During the lunar day, the Moon's surface heats up to about 390°K. When the night comes on (after 14 Earth days) the surface cools down to about 150°K within a few hours. Most of the surface, that is. Some of the large craters such as Tycho cool off much more slowly.

Astronomers have come to the conclusion that there is a thin layer of dust on most of the Moon's surface that acts as an insulating blanket. It prevents the heat stored up by the rocky material under the dust from escaping into space once the sun goes down. The body of the Moon soaks up solar heat during the long lunar day, and the dust layer prevents the heat from escaping rapidly once night falls. But the big craters apparently are new enough or deep enough so that the dust has not covered them effectively. When the sun goes down their bare rock floors radiate their stored heat immediately, and show up as hot spots on infrared detectors. The dust covered surface, meanwhile, appears much cooler because the stored heat beneath the dust is not getting up through the dust.

As we will see in the next chapter, astronauts have found that much of the Moon's surface is indeed covered with a loose sort of dust. They have left their footprints in it.

Even though IR measurements of Venus' temperature show only the temperature of the cloud tops, the infrared observations gave the first hint that Venus rotated very slowly. IR studies of the clouded planet showed that the night side of Venus was just about the same temperature as the sunlit side. If the planet rotated as rapidly as Earth, there should have been a measurable difference between the day and night temperatures. The fact that there was not indicated that the planet rotated so slowly that the heat of the sunlit side had a chance to seep over into the night side.

In 1959, IR measurements of Venus made from a manned balloon at an altitude of 24,000 meters (80,000′) showed that our sister planet's clouds contained water vapor. This was the first observation of water on another planet. Later, ground based IR studies of Mars showed some water vapor in its atmosphere.

Infrared observations of Jupiter also give only the temperature of the giant planet's cloud tops. For like Venus, Jupiter and all the giant planets are completely covered by clouds. Ammonia and methane were identified in Jupiter's clouds by optical spectroscopy. IR studies detected the presence of molecular hydrogen (H_2), which had been predicted theoretically but was invisible until it was observed by this method.

We saw in the previous chapter that the position of Jupiter's closest large satellite, Io, has an unexplained effect on the radio emissions from that planet. In 1962, it was found that the infrared energy coming out of Jupiter's clouds is as much as 30 times *stronger* in the shadow of Jupiter's moons. That is, where a moon has temporarily blocked off the incoming sunlight, the IR intensity goes up! You would expect the area being shadowed from the sun to get colder, but the region being eclipsed seemingly becomes hotter. This has baffled astronomers; to date, no reasonable explanation for it has been found.

Infrared Life on Mars?

William M. Sinton (born 1925) of the Smithsonian Astrophysical Observatory attempted to find evidence for life on Mars by infrared observations in 1956.

As we have already seen, Mars is a dry, cold world. Most of the planet is a reddish desert, although there are dark regions that Percival Lowell called "oases." The canals that Lowell and other astronomers saw are optical illusions, we know now. But is there life on Mars? The oases give indications that there might be.

The oases change color during the Martian year. Mars has seasons very much like Earth's, except that each is twice as long as ours, since the Martian year is a fraction under 687 Earth days long. Mars' day is almost identical to ours: 24 hours, 37 minutes, 22.7 seconds (our day is 3 minutes, 55.91 seconds short of 24 hours long). And Mars' seasons are due to the same cause Earth's are—a tilt of the planet's axis of 25°, 12 minutes. Earth's axis tilt is 23°, 27 minutes, 8 seconds.

In the local Martian spring, the polar cap shrinks and the dark areas in that half of the planet begin to go from their winter shade of gray to a richer, darker color—some astronomers have said that the color is a dark blue-green. This "wave of darkening" starts closest to the pole and proceeds to the equator. It looks as if moisture is released from the polar cap and used by some form of vegetation in the oases during the Martian spring and summer.

But looks can be deceiving. It would be especially foolish to expect the Martian "wave of darkening" to correspond exactly to Earthly spring blooming—unless we have solid evidence.

Sinton tried to get such evidence. He reasoned that green plants on Earth absorb certain bands of infrared radiation in the region between 3 and 4 microns. If there is Martian life, and it is composed of hydrogen and carbon—hydrocarbon compounds—such as terrestrial vegetation, then an infrared scan of the dark regions should show that some of the wavelengths between 3 and 4 microns are missing from Mars' spectrum. Energy at those wavelengths would be absorbed by the Martian vegetation.

When Sinton compared the spectrum of reflected sunlight from the bright desert regions of Mars to the spectrum of reflected sunlight from the dark oases, he found that a small amount of energy had been absorbed at 3.43, 3.56 and 3.67 microns. These are all wavelengths that are characteristic of hydrocarbon compounds.

It seemed that solid evidence for life on Mars had been found.

In 1958 he repeated the measurements, this time with more sensitive IR detectors. There were some minor corrections to the wavelengths—about 0.02 micron—but the absorption was definitely present.

Then, in 1956, it was suggested that other compounds could

cause absorption at 3.58 and 3.69 microns. Most especially, the compound deuterium oxide (heavy water) could do this. If there is a large amount of heavy water in Mars' atmosphere, it could be causing the absorption features that Sinton measured.

There is very little water, heavy or ordinary, in Mars' atmosphere. But there is plenty of it in Earth's. Sinton checked his findings and reported that heavy water in our own atmosphere could have caused the absorption he found at those two wavelengths. The 3.45 micron absorption, however, seems to be genuinely Martian in origin.

Is there life on Mars? The infrared measurements come tantalizingly close to saying "yes." But not close enough to be certain. As we will see in the next chapter, the next attack on this problem will be carried out by spacecraft borne instruments.

Infrared Stars and Protostars

The stars radiate in the infrared. In fact, the cooler the star, the more energy comes out of it in the IR region of the electromagnetic spectrum.

Hot blue stars such as Rigel radiate most strongly in the blue-violet end of the visible spectrum. There are even hotter stars that emit most of their energy in the ultraviolet. The sun's peak of energy falls at about 0.5 micron (5000 Angstroms), which is the wavelength of yellow light.

Most of the billions of stars in the Milky Way galaxy are cooler than the sun, and emit much of their energy in infrared wavelengths. We do not notice them especially in the visible wavelengths used by optical astronomers because they are very dim in that region of the spectrum. With infrared astronomy, stars and other celestial objects as cool as 1000°K and even below have been located.

If we could see the sky with IR sensitive eyes, the heavens would look very different to us. The familiar constellations of the Big Dipper and Orion, and most others, would disappear. The brilliant blue and blue-white stars such as Rigel, Sirius, Deneb, Vega and many others would be all but invisible. On the other hand, red giant stars such as Betelgeuse, Antares and Aldebaran would still be prominent. And a host of "new" stars, which cannot be seen without a telescope in the visible wavelengths, would dot the infrared sky.

Of the 300 brightest visible stars, only about 60 are also bright in the infrared. The strongest IR stars may be either genuinely cool stars, with surface temperatures as low as 1000°K, or they may be hotter stars that are screened by dust layers. In that case, what we see is light that has been scattered and absorbed by the dust: long-wavelength light tends to get through such dust screens much better

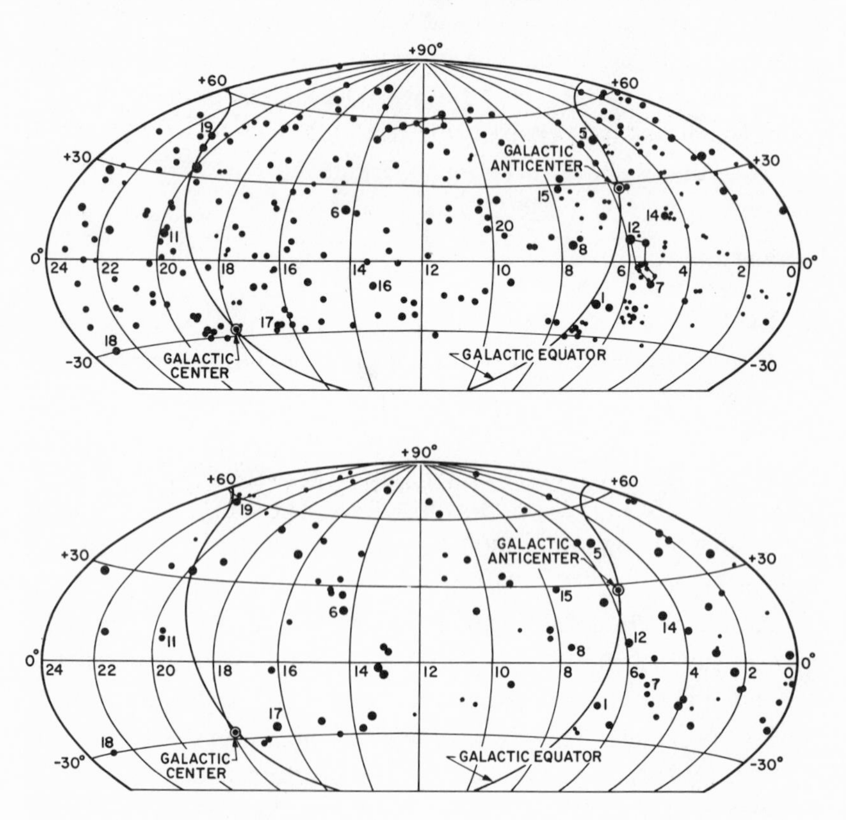

Fig. 6-2. The brightest stars of the visible sky are not the brightest stars of the infrared sky. In top drawing, the visible sky is shown, with the 20 brightest stars labelled. The infrared sky (bottom) is very different; many visibly-bright stars disappear in infrared wavelengths, and many stars too dim to be seen visibly are very bright in the infrared region of the spectrum.

than the shorter wavelengths of the blue end of the spectrum (which is why sunsets are red). Also, in some cases we may be seeing radiation from the dust itself, which absorbs the shorter wavelengths of a

Fig. 6-3. Protostar formations in the Rosette Nebula. Dark clouds of gas and dust are condensing to form new suns and solar systems. Such clouds are strong infrared emitters. (Mt. Wilson and Palomar Observatories)

nearby star and then reradiates energy in the red and infrared wavelengths.

So not all of the objects in the infrared sky are stars. Some of them, in fact, seem to be *protostars*: aggregations of gas and dust that are in the process of becoming new stars, and perhaps new planetary systems as well.

Current theories on how our solar system began picture it as starting out in a vast cloud of gas and dust. The gas was mostly hydrogen, and by "dust" astronomers mean solid grains of frozen hydrogen mixed with some heavier elements such as oxygen, carbon, silicon, metals, etc. We saw in Chapter 5 that radio telescopes have detected surprisingly complex molecules in such dust clouds, as well.

Several possible protostars have been seen in the infrared wavelengths. One of the first to be discovered is in the constellation Cygnus. At a wavelength of 2 microns, the Cygnus IR source is emitting as much energy as the brightest visible stars in the sky. Other possible protostars have been seen in the constellation Orion, which has long been known to be a breeding ground for new stars.

Most of these protostars have been found in regions that are rich in swirling gas and dust clouds, and close to the type of star that astronomers call *T Tauri*. Named after the first of its kind to be studied, in the constellation Taurus, the T Tauri stars are apparently very young. They are always found in gas-dust clouds, and they pulsate irregularly. Some astronomers believe that they are stars that are so young they have not yet settled down to a stable existence, as the Sun has.

Galactic Cores and Quasars

We saw in Chapter 5 that the center of the Milky Way galaxy is a region of strong radio emission. In the infrared wavelengths, the galactic core also appears to be an area of intense radiation and activity.

Optical studies of other galaxies have shown that they tend to have a definite bulge at their cores, where the stars are packed much more densely than they are out in the spiral arms. The core stars in galaxies are generally old and reddish. In the spiral arms—where Earth is located—are younger, bluish stars.

We cannot see the core of the Milky Way galaxy because of the vast clouds of interstellar dust that block our view. But radio and infrared observations have penetrated the dust clouds and shown us something of the heart of our galaxy.

In the densest section of the Milky Way's core the stars must be packed together about 10 million times more closely than they are here in our less crowded neighborhood: the Carina-Cygnus spiral arm. If we were situated near a star in that core there would never be darkness for us. The stars would be thousands of times brighter than the stars we know, even though they would still be about 1 lightyear apart, on the average.

This densely packed core of the galaxy radiates strongly in the infrared, as we would expect, since the stars there are mostly cool and red. Astrophysicists believe that such red giant stars are among the oldest stars in the galaxy.

IR studies have also located a tiny but powerful infrared discrete source close to the center of the Milky Way galaxy. It is apparently only 0.1 parsec in diameter, yet seems to be putting out 300,000 times the energy of the Sun. No one can explain what this might be, but it reminds many astronomers of the problems they face in trying to understand the quasars.

Other galaxies are too far away for us to detect such small "hot spots" in their cores. But the quasars are so powerful and apparently so small that they resemble the IR "hot spot" at the core of the Milky Way. Infrared studies of the quasars show that they are emitting as much or more energy in the IR as they are putting out in radio and optical wavelengths. Which just makes the problem of explaining them more difficult!

Is there some relation between the seemingly tiny, intensely powerful quasars and the core of our own galaxy? Several astrophysicists and cosmologists feel that the cores of galaxies—including our Milky Way—are centers of intense, even violent activity. And the quasars, they believe, may be very young, very distant galaxies that are in the first and most brilliant phase of core explosions.

High Energy Astronomy

Now we turn to the types of electromagnetic energy that have wavelengths shorter than visible light: ultraviolet, x-rays, and gamma rays. This is the domain that astronomers call "high energy" astronomy.

Why is it called this? To explain, we must look a bit deeper into the nature of electromagnetic energy.

Visible light, radio, UV, IR—so far in this book we have considered all electromagnetic energy only as waves. But electromagnetic energy can also be thought of as particles. Either way or both. Physicists describe such energy in the way that is most useful. Sometimes

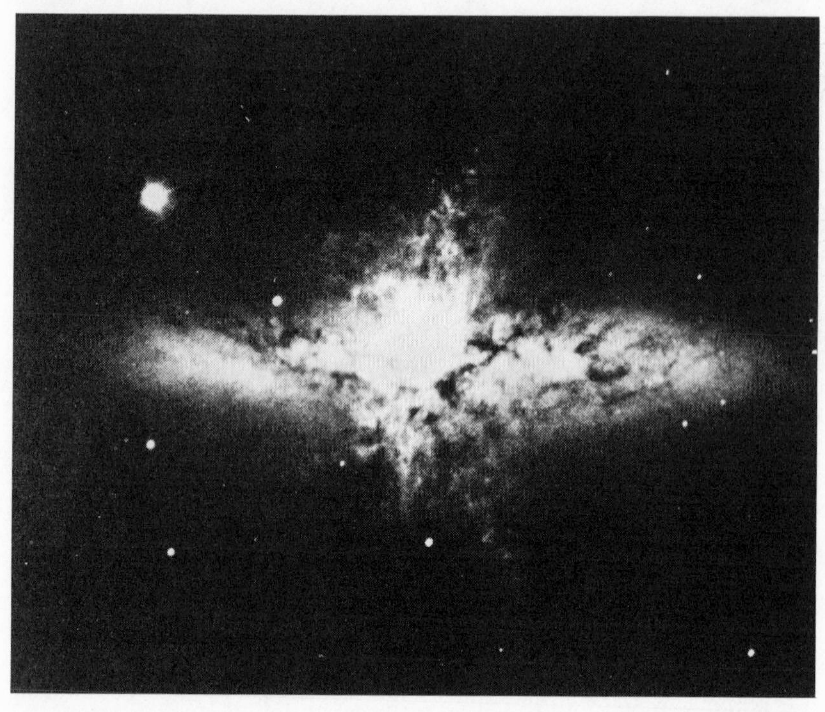

Fig. 6-4. Infrared studies of the cores of galaxies, including our own Milky Way, have shown that very violent energy releases may take place in galactic cores. Here, the small galaxy M82 is seen in the throes of an explosion that is hurling filaments of ionized hydrogen gas thousands of lightyears out from the galaxy's core. (Mt. Wilson and Palomar Observatories)

they talk about *wavicles*—energy that is at the same time both waves and particles. This may seem a strange concept to grasp, at first, but it is a cornerstone of modern physics: electromagnetic energy can be described as a wave and/or a particle at the same time.

The name given to a particle of electromagnetic energy is the *photon*. The shorter the wavelength, the more energy an individual photon carries. Thus a photon of visible light is much more energetic than a photon of radio wavelength. And, on the average, a photon at the very short wavelengths of the x-rays is about 1000 times more energetic than a photon of visible light.

These shorter wavelengths are generally measured in angstrom units. The unit is named for the Swedish physicist Anders Jonas Angstrom (1814-1874). One angstrom equals 100 millionths of a centimeter (10^{-8} cm) or 10 thousandths of a micron ($10^{-3}\mu$). Visible light runs from roughly 7500 angstroms at the red end of the optical spectrum, to 4000 angstroms in the deep violet. The ultraviolet regime is from 4000 to 300 angstroms. From 300 to 0.1 angstroms is the x-ray region of the electromagnetic spectrum. Wavelengths below 0.1 angstrom are called gamma rays.

Our atmosphere effectively blocks all wavelengths shorter than 3000 angstroms, so practically all the observations in high energy astronomy have been made from high-altitude balloons, sounding rockets (which go straight up and spend only a few minutes above the atmosphere) and satellites.

Much of the work that has been done in UV astronomy has been carried out by telescopes and other instruments placed aboard unmanned satellites. The two most successful satellite "platforms" for UV astronomy have been the Second Orbiting Astronomical Observatory (OAO-2), launched in December 1968, and the Fourth Orbiting Solar Observatory (OSO-4), launched in October, 1967.

The first target of the UV astronomers was the Sun. As we saw earlier, there is a spectacular and unexplained rise in temperature between the Sun's 6000°K photosphere and its million degree corona. Ultraviolet observations have confirmed this fact by making pinpoint measurements of the temperatures in the corona and the chromosphere, which is a thin layer of plasma that lies between the photosphere and corona. Temperatures as high as 2,000,000°K have been measured at a distance of some 200,000 kilometers out from the photosphere.

To date no one has adequately explained the non-thermal energy processes that go on in the Sun's outer regions. But UV observations have shown that sunspots have a decided influence on the temperatures in the corona. Although the sunspots themselves appear to be cooler than the photospheric plasma around them, the temperatures in the chromosphere and corona just above a sunspot are hotter than chromospheric and coronal temperatures where there are no sunspots.

OAO-2 aimed its telescopes not at the Sun, but at the stars. This satellite has provided longterm observations of some 50,000 stars in the ultraviolet wavelengths.

Although most stars are cooler and redder than the Sun, there are hot blue stars with surface temperatures of 25,000°K or more that greatly interest astronomers. These stars are young, and spend energy fast. They cannot last long, because they are using up their nuclear fuel at a prodigious rate.

For example, consider Rigel, one of the brightest stars in our sky. Rigel is 23,000 times more luminous than the Sun. This means it must be using up mass 23,000 times faster. If the Sun is converting 4 million tons of matter into energy every second, Rigel must be converting 90 billion tons of mass into energy every second. Yet Rigel is no more than 40 times the Sun's total mass. Thus Rigel will run out of nuclear fuel before the Sun does. Astronomers have estimated that Rigel cannot be much older than 10 million years, and will not last another 10 million. An eyeblink in the 10 billion year life expectancy of the Sun!

These hot blue stars, then, offer astronomers a chance to study very young stars, and at the same time a chance to observe high energy processes at work. Much of the blue stars' energy output is in the ultraviolet, and must be observed from outside the Earth's atmosphere. Rigel is putting out about 80% of its energy in UV.

UV measurements have been made of individual stars such as Rigel and Spica; of star clusters rich in young blue giants, such as the Pleiades; and of outer galaxies, particularly the great spiral, M-31, in Andromeda. For the most part these measurements have given strong observational support for theoretical ideas about the energy processes and evolution of young stars.

One interesting surprise, though, was the finding of an "ultraviolet excess" in the central regions of the Andromeda galaxy. Groundbased observations of M-31 had led to the conclusion that the core of this galaxy contained only old, red stars. The OAO-2 observations showed a surprising amount of UV radiation coming from the core, which means there must be a number of hot blue stars there, as well as the aged red giants.

The striking fact is that the UV observations, like the completely different infrared and radio studies, have also shown more things going on in the cores of galaxies than anyone had previously suspected.

While ultraviolet astronomy has not returned too many surprises,

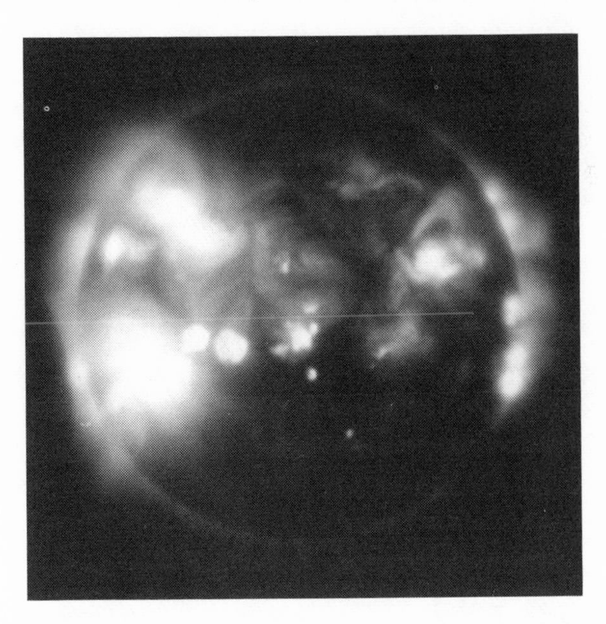

Fig. 6-5. An x-ray photograph of the Sun, taken by a rocket-borne camera. Note that much of the x-ray emission comes from beyond the photosphere, in the near corona. (American Science and Engineering)

x-ray studies of the sky have more than once startled the astronomical world.

Most x-ray observations have been made from sounding rockets, which spend only a precious few minutes above the atmosphere. Men such as Herbert Friedman (born 1916) of the Naval Research Laboratory pioneered in the development and refinement of rocket borne x-ray astronomy.

The first rockets to carry x-ray sensitive instruments above the Earth's atmosphere were not seeking astronomical knowledge. They were fired in the late 1940s to gain information about the dangerous forms of radiation that might be a hazard to men flying rocket planes and spacecraft.

The instruments showed that the Sun emits a measurable amount of x-rays. This was unexpected, and was one of the first clues to the fact that high energy processes are at work in the Sun. Astronomers now realize that the same high energy processes are associated with sunspots and solar flares, which in turn affect the Earth, as we will see in the next chapter.

Although the Sun's output of x-rays is usually only about a millionth as strong as its output of visible light, astronomers quickly

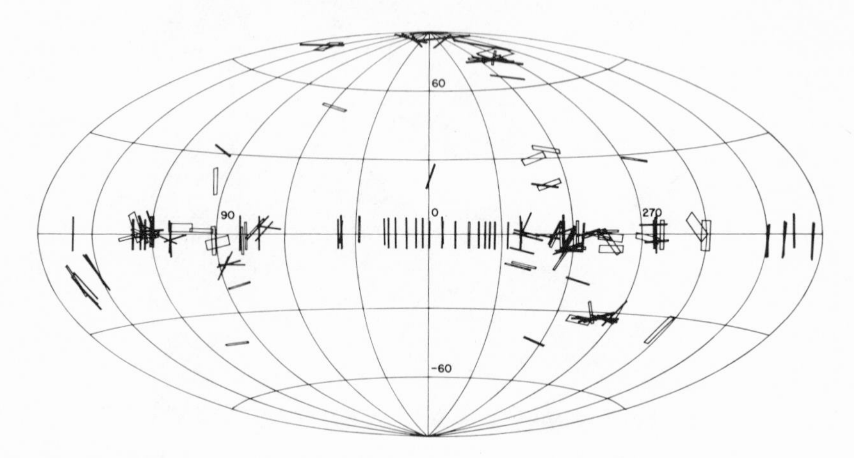

Fig. 6-6. Regions of strong x-ray emission outside the solar system, plotted on a sky map. Note that most of the x-ray sources are concentrated along the Milky Way's central plane. These observations were made from the Uhuru x-ray astronomy satellite, launched December 12, 1970. (American Science and Engineering)

decided that there might be much stronger x-ray sources in the sky. After all, the Sun is a mild mannered, stable star. There are much hotter more energetic stars in the sky—and there are more violent phenomena, such as the Crab Nebula.

In June, 1962, a team of scientists and engineers headed by Bruno Rossi (born 1905) of MIT launched an Aerobee rocket that discovered a strong x-ray source in the constellation Scorpio; 10 months later, Friedman's group found powerful x-ray emission coming from the Crab Nebula. Since then, dozens of x-ray sources have been detected.

The surprising thing about the first discovery was that the source in Scorpio, Sco X-1, is emitting a million times more x-ray energy than the Sun. Optical astronomers have found a visible star close enough to the x-ray source; they believe the two are one and the same object. The problem of identifying the visible star as Sco X-1 is that the x-ray detectors do not have a good enough resolution to pinpoint the location of the x-ray source. There are many visible stars in the region of the x-ray source.

The star that astronomers now believe is most likely to be Sco X-1 is rather dim optically: it is a 13th magnitude star, thousands of times too dim to be seen with the unaided eye. But it is emitting a thousand times more energy at x-ray wavelengths than it emits as visible light.

Astronomers immediately began asking themselves what sort of star could produce such a heavy flux of x-rays. Theoretical considerations suggested that it might be a neutron star, the collapsed core of a star that had undergone a supernova explosion. The fact that there was an x-ray source in the Crab Nebula lent some weight to this idea. Remember, this was in the mid-1960s, before the pulsars were discovered. Neutron stars were strictly a theoretical concept at that time.

Friedman and his group tried an elegant experiment to decide if the Crab Nebula was indeed a neutron star. The Moon passed in front of the Crab Nebula in July, 1964. If the x-rays had been coming from a tiny neutron star—which should have been no more than 10 to 100 kilometers in diameter—then the x-ray emission should have quickly "winked out" as the Moon passed in front of it. If, on the other hand, the x-ray signal had slowly faded out, then the x-rays would have been coming from a much wider area and not from a tiny neutron star.

The x-rays faded slowly as the Moon occulted the Crab Nebula. This led astronomers to conclude that the Crab's source could not be a neutron star.

That conclusion was not correct. Thanks to the discovery of the pulsars, we know that there is indeed a neutron star at the heart of the Crab Nebula. Its fierce energy of rotation supplies the power for much of the light and radio energy coming from the Nebula, as well as the precisely timed pulses across a wide spectrum of wavelengths. The x-ray emission stems directly from the neutron star itself. Its temperature has been calculated to be around 10 million degrees!

The lunar occultation experiment gave the wrong impression because x-rays are also coming from the plasma clouds surrounding the neutron star-pulsar; but these x-rays are triggered initially by the fantastically energetic star itself.

As we have seen, one of the problems of x-ray astronomy is that x-ray detectors do not have good resolving power. The discovery of Sco X-1 was made with detectors that had a resolving power of about 20 seconds-of-arc. Compared to the hundredth-arc-second resolution of optical and radio telescopes, x-ray detectors are myopic.

But when we go from x-rays to gamma rays, we go from myopia to near blindness. Gamma ray detectors have been flown aboard satellites such as OSO-3 and Explorer 11. The instruments found gamma radiation, all right, but they were unable to resolve discrete gamma sources with any real certainty. There is some evidence of a gamma ray source in the region of Sagittarius, but this may be merely the concentrated radiation from the core of the galaxy rather than individual gamma ray stars.

There is a broad band of gamma ray energy coming from the plane of the Milky Way, as we would expect. More than this, existing instruments cannot tell us.

While gamma rays are the most energetic form of electromagnetic radiation known, there are even more energetic particles streaking into our atmosphere from deep space. These particles are smaller than atoms; millions of them have passed through your body as you read this paragraph!

Cosmic Rays and Neutrinos

There are teams of astronomers working in mines as deep as 3 kilometers underground, studying the Sun.

To understand this rather bizarre situation, we must understand cosmic rays and neutrinos.

In the first place, cosmic "rays" are not rays at all, but particles. In the 19th century, physicists discovered that there is an unceasing shower of low level radiation—like radioactivity from elements such as radium and uranium—everywhere on Earth. At first they thought that this radiation was coming from the Sun itself, especially since it could also be detected in mines deep underground. But balloon flights showed that the radiation gets stronger higher in the atmosphere.

It became apparent that the radiation was coming from beyond the atmosphere, so it became known as cosmic radiation. Further studies showed that the radiation is not electromagnetic energy at all, but is caused by very energetic particles—bare nuclei of atoms that have been stripped of all their electrons.

Meanwhile, physicists were discovering that radioactivity from unstable atomic nuclei such as uranium also consisted mainly of particles. There are three types of radioactive "radiation:" alpha particles, which are combinations of two protons and two electrons, exactly like the nucleus of a helium atom; beta particles, which are single free electrons; and gamma rays, which we have seen are true electromagnetic radiation.

Unfortunately, the term "cosmic rays" has become entrenched in the language, and we must be careful to realize that "radiation" can often mean a stream of particles instead of electromagnetic energy.

Cosmic radiation consists mostly of single protons, bare hydrogen nucleii. Much heavier nucleii have been detected, including the nucleii of iron and other heavy metals, but hydrogen is the predominant nucleus. The ratio of hydrogen nucleii to the heavier elements is used by astronomers as one measure of the relative abundances of the elements in the universe. Together with spectroscopic analyses of starlight, cosmic radiation counts indicate that the universe is more than 99% hydrogen and helium, with a smattering of the heavier elements.

Cosmic radiation strikes every square centimeter of the Earth's surface 24 hours a day, every day. The cosmic particles are so energetic that they can often penetrate thousands of meters of solid ground. Half a dozen or more cosmic particles strike your body every minute of your life.

However, most of the cosmic radiation that reaches the Earth's surface is not the original particles from outer space. The "primary" cosmic particles almost always run into an atom or molecule in the Earth's atmosphere and cause a shattering nuclear collision that produces a shower of "secondary" particles. It is these secondaries, for the most part, that we get at the surface. To study the primary cosmic particles, astronomers have used balloons, sounding rockets, and satellites.

Where do the cosmic particles originate? Astronomers have several answers. The lowest energy cosmic particles apparently come from the sun. The higher energy particles come from beyond the solar system. Probably supernova remnants such as the Crab Nebula are breeding grounds for cosmic particles, where powerful magnetic fields can accelerate particles and then fling them out at enormous velocities. There is some suspicion that the very highest energy particles might come from beyond the Milky Way.

How energetic are they? Physicists use a term called the *electron volt* (ev) to describe the energy of subatomic particles. This is a very small unit of energy, actually. It would take 100,000 electron volts (10^5 ev) per second to equal 1 watt of power. But the cosmic particles pack billions of electron volts into their minuscule bodies. The lowest energy particles are about 10^9 ev, a billion electron volts, abbreviated as Bev. The highest energies have been at 10^{20} ev and above—a 100 billion Bev!

There is a curious relationship between sunspot activity and the intensity of cosmic radiation striking Earth. Apparently solar flares produce a flood of low energy cosmic particles, but shortly after a flare all types of cosmic radiation decrease sharply. We will see the reason for this in the next chapter.

Astronomers have been studying cosmic particles mainly because they tell us something about the nature of the universe beyond the solar system. These tiny energetic particles are messengers that come from distant stars, perhaps even more remote galaxies. They show us that there are energy producing mechanisms at work that far exceed anything the Sun has done.

While cosmic particles can tell us something of the universe outside the solar system, the elusive neutrino can tell us what is happening inside the Sun.

Neutrinos are particles that have been described as "the little man who wasn't there." They were first predicted to exist by theoretical physicists in the 1930s. Finding an actual neutrino to confirm the prediction was much more difficult to accomplish, though. It was not until 1956 that neutrinos were actually detected, using a huge nuclear power reactor as a source. Even then, it was hardly simple. Out of some 10^{17} neutrinos pouring out of the reactor each second, the experimenters picked up about 3 per hour.

The trouble with the neutrino is that it just does not interact with anything. It has no mass and no electrical charge. It penetrates solid matter as easily as light goes through a window glass; more easily, in fact. Calculations have shown that a neutrino could penetrate a wall of lead *50 lightyears thick* as if nothing were in its way!

But occasionally a neutrino just happens to hit an atom in the right way and gets stopped. This is the only way that scientists have been able to detect neutrinos.

Why bother?

Because neutrinos can tell us what is going on inside the Sun. The thermonuclear fusion reactions that power the Sun produce electromagnetic energy—sunlight—and neutrinos. The electromagnetic energy worms its way upward from the Sun's core very slowly; the sunlight we receive today began as a gamma radiation in the Sun's core many years ago. But the neutrinos, once produced at the core, fly outward immediately, completely unhampered by more than a half million kilometers of dense solar plasma!

Thus, if we can trap neutrinos from the Sun, we can perhaps begin to learn what is going on inside the Sun's core right now. But just as the recipe for an omelet begins with finding some eggs, the basis of neutrino astronomy is to find some neutrinos.

To do this, astronomers have set up elaborate equipment in deep mines. By going deep underground the neutrino hunters can screen out most of the other kinds of radiation that would interfere with their work, such as cosmic particles and other background "noise." In fact, secondary cosmic radiation includes a type of neutrino; not

Fig. 6-7. A neutrino "telescope" deep in the Homestake Mine in South Dakota. This giant vat of cleaning fluid traps neutrinos emitted by the Sun. (Brookhaven National Laboratory)

the type that the Sun produces, but close enough to cause more confusion than even a neutrino hunter deserves. So they go deep underground.

As far as solar neutrinos are concerned, it does not matter how deep underground you go. They penetrate solid rock as if it was not there. There are just as many neutrinos coming at you at midnight, when they must pass through the whole body of this planet, as there are at noon, when the Sun is directly overhead.

To catch a few neutrinos, astronomers have used a number of ingenious detectors. Perhaps the most intriguing of them is a 100,000 gallon tank of cleaning fluid in the Homestake Mine in South Dakota.

Other neutrino hunts have been made in the 3 kilometer deep gold mine at Witwatersrand, South Africa; a 2 kilometer deep gold mine in the Kolar gold fields of southern India; and in a shallower salt mine near Salt Lake City. It is no coincidence that gold mines are popular among neutrino astronomers; gold mines are the deepest mines that men have dug.

The idea behind the cleaning fluid detector at the Homestake Mine is basically simple. The cleaning fluid contains a large amount of chlorine. When a neutrino strikes a chlorine atom, it transmutes the atom into a type of argon atom that is radioactive. Thus, by measuring the mount of radioactive argon in the tank, you can tell how many neutrinos have been caught.

To date, the number of neutrinos actually captured has been far lower than those expected from calculations. This can mean one of two things: 1: the experiment is not capturing neutrinos at the predicted rate; or 2: the Sun is not producing neutrinos at the rate theoretically estimated.

The experiment itself has been checked time and again. Most astronomers are now wondering if our theories about the Sun's energy producing core might not need adjustment.

No one doubts that the Sun produces its energy by thermonuclear fusion. But the details of that process—the particular reactions going on inside the Sun, and above all the very age of the Sun—are being held up for reexamination in the "light" of the neutrino experiments.

The so called missing neutrinos may be telling us that the Sun's energy producing core is much smaller than previously believed. If so, then the Sun must be much younger than previously assumed. Or there might be reactions going on inside the Sun that simply do not produce as many neutrinos as had been assumed earlier.

Or the elusive neutrino may just be playing one of its "man who wasn't there" tricks. Only time and further investigations will tell.

Gravitational Waves

While hunting neutrinos in a gold mine is strange enough, Joseph Weber (born 1919) of the University of Maryland is scanning the Milky Way galaxy from inside a closed building. His "telescope" is a solid cylinder of aluminum, nearly a meter in diameter and 1.5 meters long; it weighs 3.5 tons.

He is searching for gravity waves.

Modern theories of physics show that gravity waves exist. In some ways they behave like electromagnetic waves: they move with the speed of light and carry energy.

When a star collapses, as most stars eventually do, it emits a strong pulse of gravitational waves. Weber and his colleagues are seeking those waves. Apparently they have found some.

This solid aluminum "telescope" is suspended from very stable iron piers and kept in a vacuum chamber. Thus no outside influences, such as the vibrations from a passing automobile or even from an air molecule, can disturb the cylinder.

Placed along the side of the cylinder are *piezo electric* sensors that can convert the tiniest motion into a measurable electrical signal. The apparatus is so sensitive that it can detect a motion as small as 100th of the diameter of an atom's nucleus!

There is a similar detector in the Argonne National Laboratory near Chicago. The two detectors work together. Only gravitational pulses felt by both detectors at the same time are considered to be coming from space. If one detector senses a gravitational pulse and the other does not, Weber and his colleagues conclude that something here on Earth made the gravitational "noise."

The "gravity telescopes" have not only detected gravitational waves from beyond the solar system, but they have found far more

Fig. 6-8. A gravity "telescope." This massive cylinder of aluminum is hung suspended in a vacuum chamber, isolated from all outside sources of motion. Gravity waves emitted by collapsing stars can make the cylinder move slightly. Piezoelectric detectors being placed along cylinder can detect motions as small as a fraction of an atom's diameter. (University of Maryland)

gravitational energy than anyone expected. Weber estimates that something like 1000 solar masses are being converted into gravitational energy each year in the Milky Way's central regions.

This means that the material of about 1000 Suns is disappearing and being turned into gravitational energy. This is far more energy than the Milky Way's core region emits in visible light or radio wavelengths!

What could be causing this? Is it really happening, or is the gravity wave experiment giving faulty information? It will take more time and refined measurements and analysis to say for certain. But the gravity wave experiment once again points toward the conclusion that the core of our galaxy may be a violent place.

What the New Eyes See

In astronomy's Second Era, the heart of our Milky Way galaxy was looked upon as a sort of old age home, where very aged red giant stars quietly spend their last few eons before sinking into darkness and oblivion.

The new astronomies of the Third Era, from infrared through gravitational wave detectors, all give strong evidence that the galaxy's core is an active region, where intense energies are at play. And there are indications that the cores of other galaxies are just as active, if not moreso.

We will examine these ideas more closely in Chapter 9. Now it is time to return our attention to the solar system, because something equally exciting is happening right here in our own celestial neighborhood. For the first time, men are not merely sitting on planet Earth and looking out passively at the universe. They are sending instruments—and men—out to the Moon and the planets.

7.

Out of This World Astronomy

The title of this chapter admittedly is rather whimsical. It is meant to convey the idea that, thanks to rockets and spacecraft, we are starting to investigate the solar system first hand instead of merely sitting on Earth and gazing out at the sky. On the Moon, at least, men and remotely controlled machines literally are shovelling samples of lunar material into return vehicles for examination on Earth.

Balloons and Sounding Rockets

As we have seen in earlier chapters, high altitude balloons and sounding rockets have been used in astronomical work for many years.

The mating of high altitude balloons and astronomy owes much to the Belgian born physicist Auguste Piccard (1884-1962) who developed a closed, spherical cabin for balloon crews—a sort of precursor to modern spacecraft cabins. In 1931, Piccard ascended to 50,000′ (15,000 meters) to study the primary cosmic rays.

In 1954, Audouin Dollfus (born 1924) of the Meudon Observatory in France carried a specially designed telescope and infrared equipment to 23,000 feet (6900 meters). His observations of Mars, the Moon and the Sun did not produce any basically new informa-

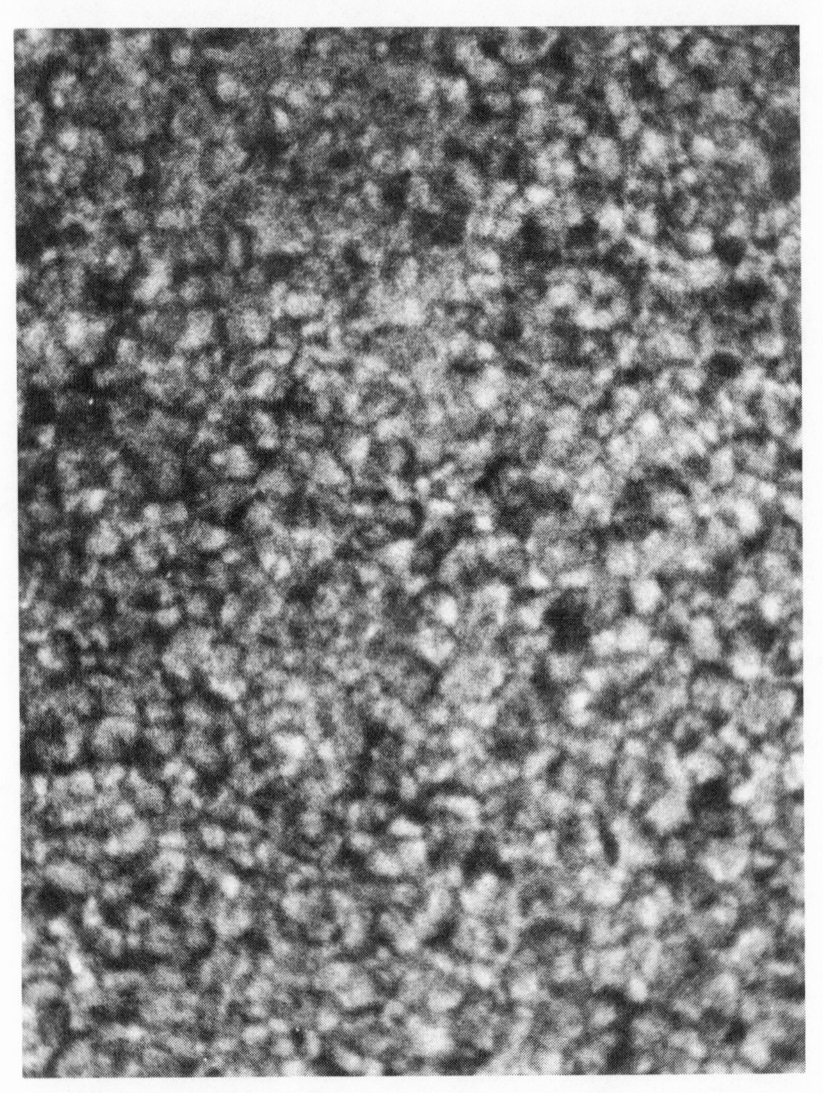

Fig. 7-1. The surface of the Sun is covered with convection cells, bubbles of 6000° K plasma boiling up from the Sun's interior. Each cell is several hundred kilometers across. (Mt. Wilson and Palomar Observatories)

tion, and Dollfus concluded that higher altitudes were necessary. But his flight showed that a balloon could be a stable enough "platform" for the successful use of an astronomical telescope.

In the United States, Martin Schwarzschild (born 1912) of Princeton University began a series of unmanned balloon flights in 1957. He called his program *Stratoscope*. The Stratoscope II balloon lifted a radio controlled 36″ (91.44 centimeters) telescope to 80,000′ (24,000 meters).

Schwarzschild's Stratoscope balloons have obtained invaluable data about the Sun, among their other functions. Visible light photographs made from Stratoscope balloons have shown that the photosphere has a granular appearance, which has been compared to oatmeal bubbling in a pot. It's an accurate comparison. Each "bubble" on the sun is a *convection cell,* a mass of hot plasma that has risen to the top of the photosphere where it cools, darkens, and sinks back to the interior. Each cell is about the size of Pennsylvania. These photographs from Stratoscope have been vital in providing evidence of how heat moves from the interior of the sun to the top of the photosphere.

As we saw earlier, a manned balloon flight in 1959, using infrared spectroscopy, first detected the presence of water vapor in Venus' clouds. Later balloon borne measurements of Venus have confirmed the presence of water vapor, although the exact amount of water content in the clouds is still being argued.

There are many fine and fantastic stories about ballooning. Launching a huge polyester bag filled with thousands of cubic feet of helium is no easy trick. Frequently the balloons have burst while being filled. Wind and weather must be perfect or the balloon can be wrecked—together with its valuable equipment. Not to mention the crew, if the balloon is manned. And there are other hazards, as well.

For example, in the late 1950s an Air Force team of scientists and engineers launced a high altitude balloon to study the effect of primary cosmic rays on human beings. Their experimental equipment included a human skull with a photographic plate mounted inside it. The idea was to see how much protection from the radiation was given by the bones of the skull. Naturally, the balloon was blown off course by unexpected winds. The men on the ground followed it cross country in a mad chase. They were afraid if the metal instrument package came down and was discovered by some good citizen, with the skull inside it, they would have a flying saucer scare on their hands that they would never live down! They got to the instrument package before anyone else did, and developed the photographic film in the basement of an empty school building. The film was streaked by several primary cosmic particles that had penetrated the metal cabin and the skull, to smash into the molecules of photographic emulsion.

While the balloonists were doing their thing, rocket engineers started working with astronomers.

Just after World War II, both the United States and Russia began using captured German V-2 rockets as high altitude probes. Originally designed to deliver an explosive warhead over a range of several hundred kilometers, the V-2 could attain altitudes of close to 200 kilometers when fired straight up.

This was far higher than balloons or any other device could reach at that time. Quickly, the war born V-2's were put to work carrying ultraviolet, x-ray and other radiation detectors, as well as ordinary cameras. As the supply of V-2's began to run out, both America and Russia started building their own high altitude sounding rockets. In the United States, some of the most successful and useful of these were the Aerobee, the Viking, and the Scout.

Satellites

Although rockets could reach much higher altitudes than balloons or aircraft, they only stayed up for a few minutes, at most. Astronomers and other scientists began to press for artificial satellites that could remain in orbit above the atmosphere indefinitely.

By 1957 both the US and USSR were working on satellite programs in conjunction with the International Geophysical Year. The IGY was an 18 month long effort by scientists all over the world to cooperate in an intensive study of our planet and its relationship with the Sun.

On October 4, 1957, Russia launched the first artificial satellite, Sputnik I. Many Americans and Western Europeans were stunned;

they had not believed that Russia could match—not to mention exceed—Western technology. A space race was started which had some of the aspects of the Cold War and others of an international soccer match. It may have been wasteful and unnecessary, but it gave astronomers all over the world a rapid buildup of satellite and spacecraft technology that has put men on the Moon and instruments on Mars and Venus. And has completely changed our view of planet Earth, the Sun, and the whole solar system.

One very important, but often overlooked, facet of space science is the technique of *telemetry*. This is the trick of getting information back from a satellite or spacecraft's sensors through radio communications.

When a balloon or sounding rocket goes up, scientists usually get the data they want by recovering the instrument package after the flight. But this is impossible when it comes to unmanned satellites and interplanetary probes. So scientists and engineers have devised a whole range of techniques by which the readings of the spacecraft's sensors are translated into coded electrical signals, which are then radioed to receiving stations on Earth. Without telemetry, most of our space research would be meaningless.

The Magnetosphere and the Solar Wind

We have seen that satellites such as the Orbiting Astronomical Observatory and Orbiting Solar Observatories are adding important data to our body of knowledge of the nature of the Sun and stars. The first satellites, though, jolted astronomers and geophysicists alike with startling new information about the Earth.

The first satellite launched successfully by the United States was Explorer I, which went into orbit January 31, 1958. Its payload was slightly less than 10 kilograms (20 pounds) of instruments—among them a geiger counter to detect radioactivity and similar high energy radiation. The geiger counter on this trip was intended to measure the intensity of cosmic radiation at orbital altitude.

Strangely, the counter showed very little radiation in space, far less than balloons had shown at much lower altitudes. And when the satellite crossed Earth's equatorial regions, the geiger counter usually went altogether silent. Another geiger counter aboard Explorer III behaved the same way.

If cosmic radiation came from outer space, how could there be less of it at a few hundred kilometers' altitude than there was in the upper atmosphere? James Van Allen (born 1914) of the State University of Iowa provided the answer. He suggested that the counters were not registering low radiation levels; in fact, he felt, the radiation levels must be so high that the counters are saturated, overwhelmed, completely swamped by the unexpectedly high levels of radiation.

Later satellites carried more sophisticated instruments into orbit and it was found that Van Allen was right: there are two vast belts of high radiation levels girdling the Earth. They were immediately named the *Van Allen radiation belts.*

Radiation in the lower Van Allen belt comes mainly from high energy protons. This lower belt is centered some 3000 kilometers above the Earth. About 15,000 kilometers out from the surface, the upper belt contains very energetic electrons. Both belts curve around and dip toward the atmosphere near the Earth's geomagnetic poles.

Although the Van Allen belts circle the globe, there is very little material in them. All the particles in both belts amount to less mass than is contained in a single human being. But the particles are very energetic. The protons in the lower belt reach energies of 20 to 40 million electron volts (Mev), which can easily penetrate a centimeter or more of lead. Sometimes these protons attain levels as high as 600 Mev. The electrons of the outer belt are usually at lower energies: about 20 to 40 thousand electron volts (Kev—the K is for *kilo*). Occasionally these electrons climb into the low Mev range. Both belts contain both electrons and protons; but the highest energies seem to be concentrated in one type of particle.

Once the Van Allen belts were discovered, scientists dusted off a prediction made half a century earlier by the Norwegian physicist Carl Stormer (1874-1957). In 1907 Stormer showed mathematically that there could be belts of ionized particles trapped by the Earth's magnetic field just outside our atmosphere. And, as we saw in Chapter 5, radio astronomers discovered an extensive Van Allen type radiation belt around Jupiter.

As early as 1896 another Norwegian physicist, Olaf K. Birkeland (1867-1917) suggested that the Sun might be shooting out streams of ionized particles that cause the Northern (and Southern) Lights—the aurorae—when they interact with the Earth's atmosphere.

Instruments aboard spacecraft such as Russia's moonbound Lunas and the American Mariners and Explorers showed that there is indeed a stream of ionized particles wafting outward from the Sun. We now call it the *solar wind*.

The solar wind usually passes Earth at a velocity of some 400 kilometers per second. It consists of fully ionized hydrogen—bare protons and electrons. By ordinary terrestrial standards, this "wind" is a vacuum: there are no more than 10 to 100 particles per cubic centimeter in interplanetary space, compared to the more than 10^{19} molecules per cubic centimeter in sea level air. Yet this "vacuum" has great energies playing through it, and the solar wind has a strong effect on Earth. Most of the energy in the solar wind is invested in the

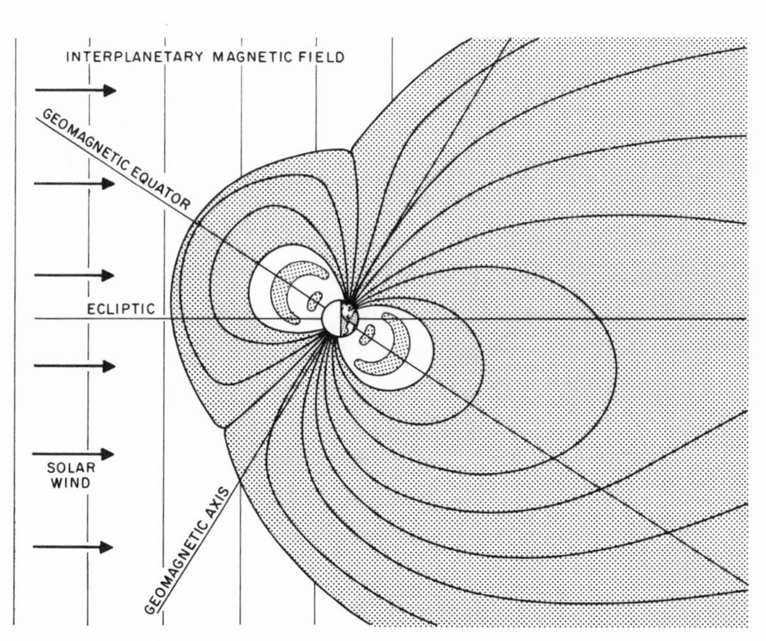

Fig. 7-2. The Earth's magnetosphere is produced by interaction of the solar wind, the Earth's magnetic field, and the trapped particles of the Van Allen radiation belts. Sunward side of the magnetosphere is pressed toward Earth by pressure of the solar wind, while the magnetosphere's "tail" stretches out beyond the orbit of the Moon.

protons, since they are nearly 2000 times more massive than the electrons. During the violent sequence of events that is involved in a solar flare, the solar wind can reach "hurricane strength" with velocities of more than 1500 kilometers per second.

The Earth creates a shock wave in the solar wind, somewhat like the bow wave made by a boat as it cuts through water. But the shock wave in the solar wind is not made by the solid body of our planet; it is made by our magnetic field, which astronomers and geophysicists call the *magnetosphere*. The solar wind presses in on the magnetosphere, flattening its sunward side and stretching the night side out into an enormous "tail" that goes past the orbit of the Moon.

When the Sun is quiet and there are few sunspots or solar flares, the "upwind" or daylight side of the magnetosphere extends out to about 10 Earth radii (one Earth radius equals 6371 kilometers). There is a shock wave standing out slightly ahead of the main body of the magnetosphere, at about 14 Earth radii. During solar disturbances the magnetosphere can be flattened by the increased pressure of the solar wind and pushed back as close as eight Earth radii.

Solar Flares and Magnetic Storms

The most violent event in the solar system is a flare on the sun. A typical solar flare will release the energy equivalent of 10 million *billion* tons of exploding TNT (10^{10} megatons).

Most flares are rather inconspicuous when viewed in visible light, although they produce intense bursts of radio energy, together with strong ultraviolet and x-ray emission. When a flare is positioned on the Sun so that it can influence the Earth, we feel its effects for several days. The magnetosphere buckles and vibrates, radiation levels in the Van Allen belts fluctuate wildly, the aurorae flame as far south as Florida, the influx of cosmic radiation is disturbed, radio communications can be disrupted for days as the ionosphere goes haywire, and any astronaut in an unshielded spacecraft outside the magnetosphere could be killed in a matter of hours, perhaps minutes.

Flares usually come from active sunspot regions. Often they erupt with no warning; on other occasions there is a gradual buildup of a glowing solar *prominence,* a seething cloud of plasma the size of a continent that hangs above the sunspot region for a half hour or so. There is generally a weak emission of x-ray and radio energy coming from the prominence.

Then the flare bursts out with an intense flash of radio, ultraviolet and x-ray emission. The plasma of the prominence is hurled away from the Sun at some 1500 kilometers per second. A surface wave surges across the photosphere, spreading outward at about 1000

Fig. 7-3. The active Sun. Prominences of glowing plasma, each of them many times larger than the Earth. (Mt. Wilson and Palomar Observatories)

kilometers per second, looking like a wave made by an underwater explosion.

The electromagnetic radiation from the flare—visible light, radio, UV, x-rays—reaches the Earth at light speed: 8.3 minutes. This is the harbinger of more serious things to come. Following the electromagnetic energy by a few minutes to a few hours is the first wave of extremely energetic protons and electrons. These particles travel through the interplanetary space at speeds that are "relativistic," or close to the velocity of light.

When they arrive at the Earth, they often burst right through the magnetosphere, which generally protects us from ionized particles by trapping them in the Van Allen belts. But solar flare particles are so energetic that they rip through the belts sometimes and are detected even at the equator, with energies of more than 15,000 Bev.

These relativistic particles are the deadliest hazard to astronauts known to exist in space. The energetic particles from a major solar flare could kill an unshielded man just as surely as could radioactive fallout from an H bomb. Men in spacecraft that orbit the Earth inside the protective shell of the magnetosphere are safe from most of this radiation. But astronauts venturing out to the Moon or to planets are exposed to the full fury of solar flare radiation.

Here on Earth's surface we are protected both by the magnetosphere and our thick atmosphere. Even so, the effects of a solar flare make themselves felt.

The incoming hail of particles rises to a maximum in a few hours, or sometimes in a few days. The intensity then tapers off gradually, over several days. The total amount of particles ejected by a flare is unknown. The largest flare ever measured, in November, 1960, showered such a flux of particles on Earth that proton counting sensors aboard balloons, rockets and satellites were swamped, just as the geiger counters that originally detected the Van Allen belts were saturated.

When a strong solar flare erupts, radio telescopes, which can work in bright sunshine and even rainstorms, are usually put out of business for several days due to the intense radiation interference.

But the most violent effects of the flare are yet to come.

The flare has ejected a great puff of plasma that travels across interplanetary space, expanding as it heads outward from the sun. When this plasma cloud impinges on the Earth's magnetosphere, it shakes the whole geomagnetic field and causes what is called a "magnetic storm." The trapped particles in the Van Allen belts are suddenly dumped into the atmosphere, where they make flaming auroral dis-

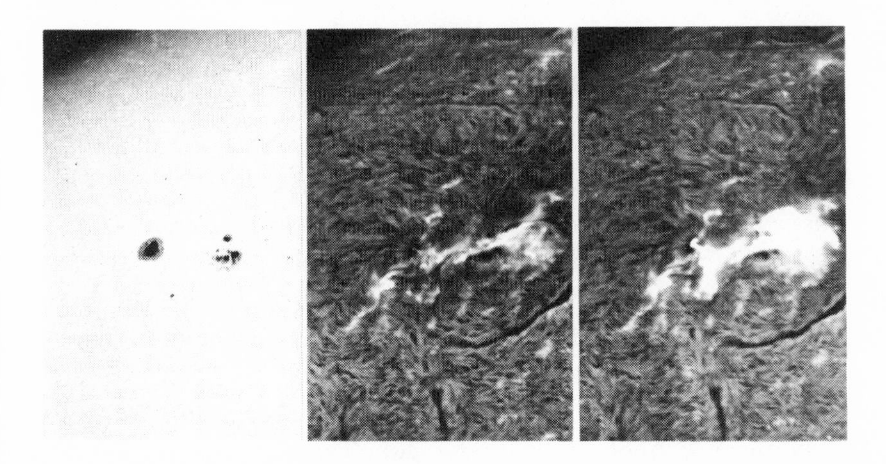

Fig. 7-4. A solar flare. Left photo shows a sunspot in ordinary light. Center photo shows same region in red light of hydrogen emission. The same area, eleven minutes later (right) emits a flare of intensely excited hydrogen. (Mt. Wilson and Palomar Observatories)

plays, often over parts of the world that never see aurorae otherwise. The ionosphere runs amok, gaining and losing ionized particles in a wildly unpredictable fashion that makes a shambles of long range radio broadcasts which rely on stable ionospheric reflecting layers.

Even the steady infall of cosmic particles is disturbed at this point. The plasma cloud shunts aside or absorbs most of the cosmic particles coming toward Earth. This phenomenon, which can last for a day or so, is known as the *Forbush decrease,* after the American physicist Scott E. Forbush (born 1904) who first noticed that cosmic radiation intensity often falls abruptly during a magnetic storm.

Within a few days, everything settles back to normal. The plasma cloud dissipates or moves on; the Van Allen belts refill and stabilize; the ionosphere calms down and radio reception becomes good again. Until the next flare.

The Moon: Astronomy Plus Geology Equals Selenography

Pick-and-shovel astronomy is well underway on the Moon. Geologists have been studying lunar rocks and soil samples returned by astronauts and unmanned retrievers. Strictly speaking, geology is the study of the Earth's solid body (*geo* is a Greek root for Earth). Therefore the study of the Moon's crust and interior is properly called *selenography,* after Selene, a Greek lunar goddess.

The Moon was the first target of the Space Race between the United States and Russia. As early as September 1959, not even two years after the first Sputnik, the Russians crash landed Luna 2 on the Moon's surface. It was the first time a manmade object had reached another celestial body. By the following October Luna 3 had given mankind a first look at the far side of the Moon.

As Table 7-1 shows, the Moon has been showered with a variety of Lunas, Zonds, Rangers, Surveyors, and Lunar orbiters, in addition to the manned Apollo vehicles. On July 20, 1969, Astronaut Neil Armstrong gained immortality as the first man to step onto the Moon's surface.

Since then a number of Apollo manned spacecraft and unmanned Russian vehicles have touched down on the Moon. They have collected samples of lunar rock and soil and returned them to Earth for scientific study. We are now able to build up a reasonable picture of the Moon's structure and history. Much of this picture remains hazy or even blank; there are still tantalizing mysteries about the Moon, and no doubt there will continue to be for many decades to come. But some basic facts about the Moon now seem to be fairly certain.

The Moon's surface shows great variations in appearance and structure. Even with the naked eye we can see dark patches and broad bright areas. The dark regions have been called *maria* ever since people actually thought they might be watery seas. The bright regions are mountainous, and are called *highlands* for obvious reasons.

All of the Moon is pockmarked with craters, some as small as a few centimeters across. The maria are actually gigantic craters, hundreds of kilometers across. Apparently the Moon was bombarded

TABLE 7-1. LUNAR PROBES, ORBITERS AND LANDERS

Name	*Launch Date*	*Mission*
Luna 1	2 January 1959	Passed within 6000 km of Moon 4 January 1959
Pioneer 4	3 March 1959	Passed within 60,000 km of Moon
Luna 2	12 September 1959	Crash-landed on Moon 13 September 1959
Luna 3	4 October 1959	First photographs of far side of Moon, 10 October 1959
Ranger 3	26 January 1962	Failed to reach Moon
Ranger 4	23 April 1962	Crash-landed on far side of Moon
Ranger 5	18 October 1962	Failed to reach Moon
Luna 4	2 April 1963	Passed within 8500 km of Moon 6 April 1963
Ranger 6	30 January 1964	Impacted on Sea of Tranquility 2 February 1964; failed to send photos
Ranger 7	28 July 1964	Impacted on Sea of Clouds 31 July 1964; transmitted 4316 photos to Earth
Ranger 8	17 February 1965	Impacted on Sea of Tranquility 20 February 1965; transmitted 7137 photos
Ranger 9	21 March 1965	Impacted in Crater Alphonsus 24 March 1965; transmitted 6150 photos
Luna 5	9 May 1965	Impacted on Sea of Clouds 12 May 1965
Luna 6	8 June 1965	Passed within 160,000 km of Moon
Zond 3	18 July 1965	Photographed lunar surface from 9220 km distance

Note: U.S. spacecraft include Pioneer, Ranger, Surveyor, Lunar Orbiter, and Apollo. Russian spacecraft are Luna and Zond.

TABLE 7-1. LUNAR PROBES, ORBITERS AND LANDERS (cont.)

Name	*Launch Date*	*Mission*
Luna 7	4 October 1965	Impacted on Ocean of Storms 7 October 1965
Luna 8	3 December 1965	Impacted on Ocean of Storms 6 December 1965
Luna 9	31 January 1966	First soft landing on Moon, Ocean of Storms; transmitted photos from lunar surface
Luna 10	31 March 1966	First artificial satellite of Moon
Surveyor 1	30 May 1966	Landed in Flamsteed Crater 2 June 1966; transmitted photos from surface
Lunar Orbiter 1	10 August 1966	Artificial satellite of Moon
Luna 11	24 August 1966	Artificial satellite of Moon
Surveyor 2	20 September 1966	Crashed on Moon 23 September 1966
Luna 12	22 October 1966	Artificial satellite of Moon
Lunar Orbiter 2	6 November 1966	Artificial satellite of Moon
Luna 13	21 December 1966	Landed on Ocean of Storms 24 December 1966
Lunar Orbiter 3	5 February 1967	Artificial satellite of Moon
Surveyor 3	17 April 1967	Landed on Ocean of Storms 20 April 1967
Lunar Orbiter 4	4 May 1967	Artificial satellite of Moon
Surveyor 4	14 July 1967	Crashed on Moon 17 July 1967
Lunar Orbiter 5	1 August 1967	Artificial satellite of Moon
Surveyor 5	8 September 1967	Landed on Sea of Tranquility 11 September 1967; first chemical analysis of lunar soil
Surveyor 6	7 November 1967	Landed in Central Bay; same mission as Surveyor 5
Surveyor 7	7 January 1968	Landed in Crater Tycho; same mission as Surveyor 5
Luna 14	7 April 1968	Artificial satellite of Moon
Zond 5	14 September 1968	Circled around Moon carrying living organisms and returned to Earth

TABLE 7-1. LUNAR PROBES, ORBITERS AND LANDERS (cont.)

Name	*Launch Date*	*Mission*
Zond 6	10 November 1968	Circled Moon and returned to Earth
Apollo 8	21 December 1968	First manned mission to Moon; circled Moon and returned to Earth
Apollo 10	18 May 1969	Manned flight to within 15 km of lunar surface
Apollo 11	16 July 1969	First manned landing on Moon, 20 July 1969
Luna 15	13 July 1969	Crashed on Sea of Crises 21 July 1969 after 52 orbits around Moon
Zond 7	7 August 1969	Same mission as Zond 6
Apollo 12	14 November 1969	Landed on Ocean of Storms 19 November 1969
Apollo 13	11 April 1970	Failed to reach lunar surface; equipment malfunction
Luna 16	12 September 1970	Landed unmanned "scientific station" on Moon; returned soil and rock samples to Earth
Luna 17	10 November 1970	Landed unmanned roving vehicle on Sea of Rains 17 November 1970; conducted remotely-directed studies of lunar surface for many months
Apollo 14	31 January 1971	Landed at Fra Mauro 5 February 1971
Apollo 15	25 July 1971	Landed near Lunar Appenines 30 July 1971
Luna 18	7 September 1971	Crashed in lunar highlands 11 September 1971

with meteoroids of huge size when it first was formed. And it is still being pelted today, as the Apollo seismometers have shown. Most of the material hitting the Moon (and Earth) is microscopically small, dust grains. These micrometeoroids are grinding down the lunar mountains and smoothing the craters, acting as a force of erosion on a world where there is no wind nor water to wear down the mountains.

The maria are made of different material than the highlands; this is obvious from even a naked eye glance. From measurements made by some of the unmanned spacecraft that have landed on the Moon, from the orbiters, and from the rock samples returned to Earth, selenologists have started to put together an understanding of the Moon's surface structure.

The maria are apparently composed of basaltic rock, heavy dark material much like the basalts of Earth. The highlands are made of lighter, brighter colored rock, sometimes called anorthosite. It is now believed that the basic underlying crust of the Moon is basaltic, and the lighter anorthosite rides atop the denser basalts. This situation is similar to that on Earth, where our continents are made of comparatively light granitic rocks that are riding atop denser basalts. The ocean floors of Earth are basaltic.

The Lunar Orbiter spacecraft and Russian orbiters showed before the first astronauts landed that the maria are comprised of denser rock than the highlands. An orbiting satellite is a very sensitive gravity measuring device. When it passes over an area of dense material, where the gravitational pull is slightly stronger than elsewhere, the satellite is slightly deflected from its path.

The spacecraft orbiting the Moon showed just such behavior when they crossed over the maria. Astronomers and astronautical engineers began talking about mass concentration, or *mascons,* on the Moon. The mascons show that the maria must be composed of material that is denser than the highlands. Might part of this "extra" density be due to the remains of the meteroids that presumably caused the maria? Such meteoroids would probably have heavy concentrations of metals in them.

When Neil Armstrong planted the first human bootprints on the Moon, he found himself walking on a loose, powdery kind of soil that he described as being "something like sand at the beach." His description was more accurate than he knew.

That sandy lunar soil is created in much the same way that beach sand is created, by the grinding down of rocks into a fine powder. But the forces of erosion stem from very different sources on the Moon. On a terrestrial beach, the rocks are ground down into sand by the action of wind and water. On the Moon, the erosion is caused by the constant infall of meteoric dust. With no atmosphere to shelter them, the lunar rocks have been sandpapered for billions of years by meteoric dust erosion.

Selenographers call this layer of soil that has been built up over the Moon's rocky crust a *regolith.* The lunar regolith might be as much as 20 meters deep in the broad basins of the maria. In the highlands, it is assumed to be more shallow, although the astronauts of Apollo 15 kicked up plenty of dust in their travels near the base of the Lunar Appenine Mountains. In the highlands, the rims of relatively new craters and the peaks of tall mountains poke out above the dusty regolith, and are probably bare rock.

The Moon is the same age as the Earth, about 4.5 to 5.5 billion years old. This estimate comes from several lines of investigation, the most definite of them being the technique of *radioactive dating.*

To understand the radioactive dating technique, we must know a little bit more about the nucleus of the atom. Most elements come in a variety of *isotopes.* That is, the nuclei of an element's atoms might have a varying number of neutrons in it. For example: hydrogen is the simplest element. Its atom consists of a single proton for a nucleus and a single electron orbiting it. There is a form of heavy hydrogen called *deuterium,* which has one proton and one neutron in the nucleus. A still heavier form of hydrogen is *tritium*, which has two neutrons in the nucleus with the one proton. Deuterium and tritium are still isotopes of hydrogen, because all three types of atoms have one proton in the nucleus and one orbital electron. Change that to two protons and two electrons and you have a completely different element—helium, which has an entirely different chemical behavior than hydrogen.

Many elements come in different isotopes. There are oxygen 16 and oxygen 15; 15 has one less neutron than its more abundant brother (and other possible oxygen isotopes, as well). There is uranium 238 and the rarer but more fissionable uranium 235. The numbers are the isotope's *atomic weight*: they are derived by adding the number of protons and neutrons in the isotope's nucleus.

Radioactive atoms spontaneously break down, or *decay*, by emitting particles from their nucleii. Over the course of time, uranium finally becomes lead. One radioactive isotope of the metal rubidium —rubidium 87—eventually decays into strontium 86. Physicists know how long it takes a given amount of one radioactive isotope to transmute itself into another element's isotopes. For example, if you take a certain amount of uranium 235, in 700 million years half of it will have decayed into various isotopes of lead. This period of time is called the *half life* of the radioactive isotope. Rubidium 87's half life is 50 billion years—it decays into strontium 86 very slowly.

By measuring the abundance of rubidium 87 to strontium 86, and knowing how long it takes to produce the strontium isotope, it is possible to calculate the age of the original rubidium. Selenologists have used this type of radioactive dating technique to determine the age of the lunar rocks.

Radioactive dating techniques have been used quite successfully here on Earth, and checked against other geological methods of estimating the ages of rock formations, so the radioactive dating technique is accepted as valid by geologists, astronomers, and selenologists. There are some uncertainties in the technique, to be sure, but it has produced viable results. And in the case of the lunar rocks, it is the most reliable method for dating the samples returned to Earth.

Most of the rocks returned to Earth from the Moon range from 3 to 3.5 billion years old. One rock, sample number 15415 from the Apollo 15 mission, has been dated at about 4.15 billion years of age. This has been dubbed the "Genesis rock": it is the oldest piece of the universe that human beings have ever handled. Allowing the Moon about a billion years to form a stable crust after it first solidified, the Genesis rock firmly shows that the Moon, like the Earth, is between 4.5 and 5.5 billion years old.

On Earth, such ancient surface rocks have long ago been ground to dust by the forces of weather, water, or vulcanism. But the vacuum protected Moon is a comparatively tranquil place—for rocks, at least.

The Moon is just as airless and waterless as Earth based astronomers had foretold. The solar wind impinges directly on the lunar surface, except when the Moon is on the night side of Earth and the magnetosphere's long "tail." Astronauts have set up equipment to measure the solar wind on the Moon; there is no atmosphere to interfere with the incoming particles.

Nor does the Moon have a magnetic field strong enough to deflect even the ephemeral solar wind. Magnetometers carried aboard spacecraft that orbited the Moon could detect only a very weak lunar magnetic field. Measurements carried out on the surface have shown that the Moon's magnetic field is less than 1% as strong as the Earth's. Moreover, there are two types of magnetic field on the Moon, neither of them like the Earth's.

The Earth has a *dipole* field, as if a huge bar magnet had been jammed through our planet, with its north and south magnetic poles near our north and south geographic poles. The weak permanent magnetic field of the Moon varies markedly from place to place, and does not add up to a form a single overall Moon-wide field. Rather, it appears that these individual magnetic fields are due to local sources of magnetism—perhaps the remains of heavy metallic meteorites that struck the Moon eons ago and blasted out the major craters.

There are also temporary magnetic fields to be found on the Moon's surface. These are thought to be caused by electrical currents underground, which in turn may be generated by the action of the solar wind or solar flares.

The weakness of the lunar magnetic fields, plus the fact that there is no planetary field as there is on Earth, has convinced some scientists that the Moon's interior is cold throughout. Earth has a core of molten metals, mostly iron, in which electrical currents constantly flow. It is presumed that this core is where Earth's magnetic field originates: the electrical currents in the core act as a dynamo to produce a permanent magnetic field. The Moon may never have had a molten core, since it is much smaller than the Earth and apparently has much less metal in its interior. The Moon's overall density is 3.33 times that of water, compared to the Earth's 5.52; this indicates that the Moon lacks heavier elements.

At first the Moon seemed to be absolutely waterless. No one expected to find liquid water on the surface, and detailed studies of the lunar rocks returned to Earth showed that they did not even have water molecules attached to them chemically, as most Earth rocks do. Chemists call this form of molecular water-carrying a *hydrate*. The first lunar rocks showed no trace of hydrates.

But, starting in March 1971, instruments left on the lunar surface by the Apollo 12 and 14 astronauts have detected what might be water vapor.

The instruments are called SIDE, which stands for Suprathermal Ion Detector Experiment. Basically, the SIDE equipment detects ions—atoms that have lost one or more electrons. The SIDE detectors have monitored and recorded many types of ions, including some impinging on the Moon's surface from space, and others vented as gases from the Apollo spacecraft themselves.

On several occasions, both the Apollo 12 and Apollo 14 SIDES picked up ions that have been tentatively identified as water vapor. Presumably, according to Earthbound scientists, the water vapor is escaping from deep inside the lunar crust. They point out that it is significant that the water "geysers" occur mainly during moonquakes. Although the "geysers" are ghostly thin and invisible to telescopes and cameras, the thin spurts of water vapor apparently come up through cracks in the crust during lunar quakes.

The Apollo 15 crew also left a SIDE detector on the Moon, but theirs has not recorded any water vapor. It might be significant, though, that the Apollo 15 equipment is located far north of the Apollo 12 and 14 sites, and 15 is in a highland region, while 12 and 14—although some 180 kilometers apart—are both in low, flat *maria* type terrain.

The SIDE discovery of water vapor may indicate that there *are* pools of water deep underground on the Moon. But as we will see in the next few paragraphs, there are important pieces of evidence that indicate that the Moon is cold and solid throughout, without a liquid core. Is the water really liquid, or is it ice? Are the SIDE instruments actually detecting water, or is it all a mistake? At this writing, the feelings of most selenologists is that the SIDE equipment has really found water.

Nothing could be more important to men who want to explore the Moon. If water can be obtained on the Moon easily enough, and in large enough quantities, then the entire nature of lunar exploration will be changed. Astronauts can stay on the Moon for extended periods of time, and ultimately even electrolyze water into hydrogen-oxygen rocket propellants. Sufficient water on the Moon could mean the successful establishment of long term outposts there, perhaps even outright colonization.

While the possibility of finding water on the Moon is enormously exciting, the most startling result of lunar exploration so far has been the manmade moonquakes. Seismologists wanted to see if the Moon's crust behaved the same as the Earth's does, so among the first experimental apparatus carried aboard the Apollo Landing Modules were seismometers, to measure any crustal motions of the lunar surface. Astronauts also laid out strings of tiny explosive charges so that the Earthbound seismologists could study the effects of a known amount of energy on the motions of the crust. The seismometer readings are automatically telemetered back to receiving stations on Earth.

Then an even more elegant experiment was thought of. The Lunar Module ascent stage, which carries the astronauts off the Moon, back to a rendezvous with the Command Module return ship, was deliberately crashed into the Moon on the Apollo 12 mission, after the astronauts had finished using it. Seismologists could calculate very precisely the amount of energy invested in the lunar Module as it power dived back into the Moon's surface.

The results staggered them. The moonquake lasted 55 minutes! Nothing like this had even happened on Earth, where quakes last a few minutes, at most.

On the Apollo 14 mission, the spent third stage of the Saturn rocket booster was deliberately fired at the Moon. It hit with an impact equal to the explosion of 11 tons of TNT. The entire Moon vibrated for 3 hours, down to a calculated depth of 35 to 40 kilometers below the surface.

"The whole Moon rang like a gong," said one awed seismologist.

The Apollo 14 Lunar Module's ascent stage was also fired back at the Moon after the astronauts had left it for good. It hit with an impact equivalent to the explosion of 725 kilograms of TNT, and caused tremors that lasted for 90 minutes. On the Apollo 15 mission, once again the Saturn upper rocket stage and the Lunar Module ascent stage were driven into the Moon's surface, causing long lasting quakes that were dutifully recorded by the seismometers left behind by the Apollo 12 and 14 astronauts. The moonquakes behaved almost exactly as theory predicted they would; the theory was based on the assumption that the Moon is of rather uniform structure in its interior, and is cold throughout.

The seismometers left on the Moon have also telemetered back to Earth a record of moonquakes that happen every month, on a nearly exact schedule. Each month, 5 days before perigee—the point of the Moon's orbit where it comes closest to Earth—and 3 days after perigee, a series of moonquakes rock the lunar surface. 80% of the quakes recorded by the Apollo seismometers come at these two times of the month. Apparently there is some gravitational tidal force that affects the Moon's interior structure when our natural satellite comes closest to us.

Incidentally, the seismometers have also picked up the tremors caused by the impact of meteoroids on the Moon's surface. Most of them seem to be hitting on the far side, which we cannot see from Earth. Oddly, the biggest meteor craters, and the greatest number of large craters, are on the side facing us. Why is this? No answer yet.

The seismic evidence points strongly to the fact that the Moon has no molten core and is cold throughout. On Earth, seismic waves are damped out and absorbed by differences in density between one layer of the Earth's structure and another, and by the Earth's molten core. On the Moon, the damping mechanisms are much weaker, allowing quakes to last much longer. A cold rocky body would behave the way the Moon does.

Waterless, airless, racked by huge temperature changes from day to night, blasted by meteoroids and all forms of radiation, the Moon does not seem a likely haven for life.

But in mid-1971 a team of biochemists announced that they had found traces of organic chemicals in a sample of soil returned from the Moon!

The team was headed by Bartholomew Nagy (born 1927) of the University of Arizona and Harold Urey (born 1893) of the University of California at La Jolla. Urey is a Nobel Prize laureate, a chemist

TABLE 7-2. INTERPLANETARY PROBES

Name	*Launch Date*	*Arrival Date*	*Closest Approach*	*Mission*
Venus 1	12 February 1961	—	—	Radio contact lost 7.5 million km from Earth
Mariner 2	26 August 1962	14 December 1962	41,000 km	First probe of Venus
Mars 1	1 November 1962	—	—	Radio contact lost 106 million km from Earth
Zond 1	2 April 1964	—	—	Failed to return data from Venus
Mariner 3	5 November 1964	—	—	Failed to reach Mars
Mariner 4	28 November 1964	14 July 1965	10,000 km	First Mars probe
Zond 2	30 November 1964	—	—	Failed to return data from Mars
Venus 2	12 November 1965	17 February 1966	24,000 km	Reached Venus but failed to return data
Venus 3	16 November 1965	1 March 1966	impact	First spacecraft to impact on another planet (Venus); failed to return data
Venus 4	12 June 1967	18 October 1967	impact	Failed to return data
Mariner 5	14 June 1967	19 October 1967	3980 km	Venus probe
Venus 5	5 January 1969	16 May 1969	impact	Failed to return data
Venus 6	10 January 1969	17 May 1969	impact	Failed to return data
Mariner 6	24 February 1969	30 July 1969	3390 km	Mars probe
Mariner 7	27 March 1969	3 August 1969	3500 km	Mars probe
Venus 7	7 August 1970	15 December 1970	landing	First successful landing on another planet (Venus)
Mariner 9	30 May 1971	13 November 1971	1395 km	First orbit of another planet (Mars)
Mars 2	19 May 1971	27 November 1971	1375 km	18-hour orbit
Mars 3	28 May 1971	2 December 1971	1500 km	11-day orbit; landed capsule on Mars 2 Dec 71

who has spent much of his life investigating astronomical problems and the question of extraterrestrial life. Nagy has been a center of controversy ever since his announcement in 1961 of finding in meteorites biological materials that were once living spores.

We will look at the meteorite controversy later in this chapter. For now, we must note that Nagy and his colleagues claim only to have found complex carbon based compounds in a sample of lunar soil—not living matter, or even material that was once alive, only organic chemicals. But all living creatures are composed of organic chemicals—long chain, carbon-based molecules. If organic compounds have been found on the Moon, can there be life there too?

The chances are strongly against it. But only much more extensive exploration will tell us for certain.

Venus: the Hothouse Planet

Ground based optical and infrared studies of the planet Venus have always been frustrating. Like her namesake, Venus is beautiful but quite mysterious behind her veil of clouds.

For generations astronomers referred to Venus as our sister planet, because Venus is not only the closest planet to us in terms of distance, it is also about the same size and density as Earth. Balloon infrared observations showed that those brilliant white clouds have at least some water vapor in them—again, like Earth.

Then the radio astronomers showed that Venus' surface is much hotter than anyone had suspected—as hot as 800°K. But some scientists claimed that the radio observations were actually coming from particles in the planet's upper atmosphere. Instead of a hot surface, they pictured a hot ionosphere. The two points of view were debated —hotly.

The advent of the space age made it possible to consider sending instruments to Venus to resolve the controversy.

The Russians were the first to try. Their Venus 1 spacecraft, launched February 12, 1961, went past Venus on a "flyby" trajectory. No information about the planet's temperature was sent back to Earth, but Venus 1 did find that the planet had no detectable magnetic field.

The "hot surface" versus the "hot ionosphere" argument was settled the next year, when, on December 14, 1962, Mariner 2 flew to within 41,000 kilometers of Venus.

The key equipment aboard Mariner 2 was a microwave radiometer, which received radio emissions from Venus at two wavelengths: 13.5 and 19 millimeters. The microwave experiment was ingenious and very successful, and it could only be done from a spacecraft close to Venus.

The experiment depended on a phenomenon known as *limb darkening*. Consider the way the planet Venus looked to the approaching spacecraft. As the craft's instruments look at the center of the planet's disk, they are looking straight down through the atmosphere to the surface. Never mind that the cloudy atmosphere is opaque to optical instruments; the important factor is that the least amount of atmosphere between the spacecraft and the surface is right at the center of the planet's disk.

As the instruments shift their aim away from the center of the disk and toward the edge (called the *limb* by astronomers) they are looking at more and more atmosphere before reaching the surface. Finally, right at the very edge of the limb, they are seeing nothing but atmosphere; the line of sight has now passed beyond the edge of the planet's solid body.

If the high microwave temperatures had been caused by a hot ionosphere, then the Mariner microwave radiometer would have seen a limb brightening effect as it scanned across Venus' disk. That is, the microwave emission would have been lowest right at the center of the disk, where the instrument was looking through the thinnest amount of atmosphere, and would have become stronger and brighter as the instrument looked further out toward the limb.

But if the temperature had indeed been coming from the surface of Venus, then the microwave scan should have shown the brightest return from the center of the disk and a limb darkening effect as the radiometer swung away from the center.

The Mariner microwave observations showed a definite limb darkening. The high temperature comes from a hot surface.

Mariner 2 also carried an infrared radiometer for measuring temperatures in Venus' clouds, and 4 other sets of experimental equipment to study the magnetic fields in interplanetary space and around Venus, to measure cosmic radiation, the solar wind, and to sample the amount of cosmic dust between Earth and Venus.

The infrared radiometer was sensitive to radiation in the wavelengths of 8 to 9 microns and 10 to 10.8 microns. These measurements showed that Venus' cloud layer must be about 24 kilometers thick, with the base of the clouds some 70 kilometers above the surface. Clearly, Venus' atmosphere must be much denser and deeper than our own, to support such a cloud deck. Early estimates were that the atmospheric pressure on Venus' surface must be at least 20 times that of Earth. The cloud temperatures range from about 200°K (-70°F) at the top to some 450°K (200°F) at the base.

Mariner 2 made no direct measurement of water vapor in the clouds, but scientists estimated from indirect evidence that there could not be more than 1/1000 of the water vapor that is present in Earth's atmosphere. As previously seen by Earth based instruments, the Mariner measurements showed that Venus' temperature varies

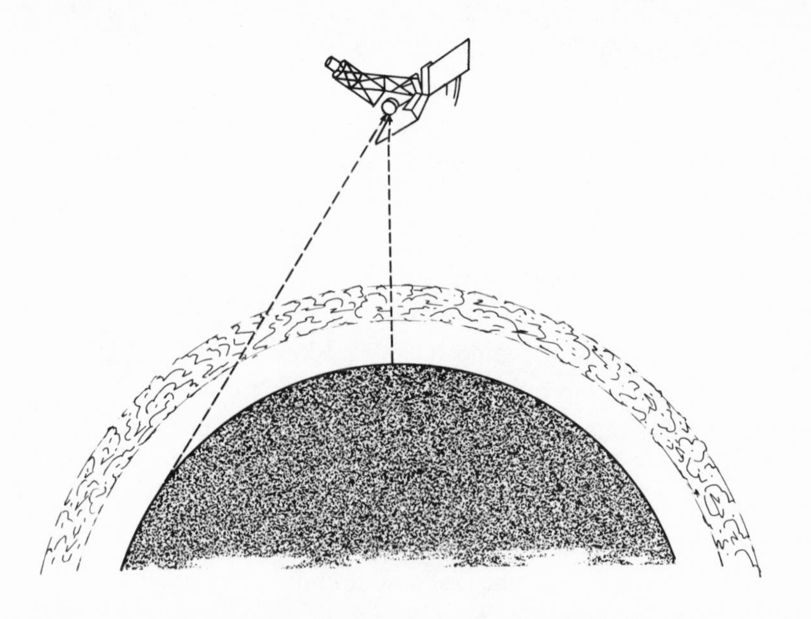

Fig. 7-5. The Venus limb darkening experiment of Mariner 2. As it flew past Venus, the spacecraft's sensors scanned the disk of Venus. Highest temperature came from center of disk, where atmosphere is thinnest, thus proving that Venus' high temperature comes from the planet's surface, not its atmosphere.

little from dayside to nightside. This showed that the planet was rotating slowly, giving the thick atmosphere time to carry heat all the way around the planet.

Since Mariner 2 was the first probe to return detailed information about Venus' surface temperature and atmospheric structure, its results far overshadowed the data sent back by the later Russian Venus probes and the American Mariner 5. In essence, these later spacecraft verified the basic findings of Mariner 2 and started filling in more of the details. The atmosphere of Venus was indeed found to be very hot and dense, and to be composed mainly of carbon dioxide —excellent "greenhouse" material. Some investigators concluded that the clouds of Venus were made more of oily, petroleum-like chemicals than of water vapor. Some jokesters began referring to Venus as the smog planet.

But while the American "flyby" Mariners were very successful, the Russians were aiming at a more ambitious goal: they wanted to land an instrument filled package on the surface of Venus.

Venus 3 crash landed on the planet, the first manmade object from Earth to touch another planet. Venus' 4 through 6 either flew directly into the cloudy atmosphere or ejected capsules into the clouds. Apparently none of them survived all the way down to the surface. They were either crushed by the enormous atmospheric pressures or their parachutes were burned up by the heat of the lower atmosphere.

But the Russians persevered and on December 15, 1970, were rewarded with success. Venus 7 touched down on the surface and started transmitting information about our "sister planet." A description of hell is what it sounds like.

Venus 7 descended through the murky atmosphere on a parachute designed to withstand temperatures as high as 800°K. The descent took 35 minutes, once the chute was opened—some 25 minutes less than the Russian engineers had expected. They believe that Venus 7 may have landed on a mountaintop, or a high plateau.

The temperature at the touchdown point was recorded at 747°K (roughly 890°F). The atmospheric pressure was some 90 kilograms per square centimeter, or about 1300 pounds per square inch. This is nearly 100 times greater than the 14.7 pounds per square inch of

Earth's sea level atmospheric pressure. The surface pressure of Venus' atmosphere is comparable to the pressure in our oceans at a depth of one kilometer. And this may be the situation on a mountaintop, thousands of meters above "sea level" on Venus!

A dark, utterly dry world, where the surface temperature is high enough to melt lead or zinc; a world that rotates backwards; a world where the air is more like molten lava than anything else; this is our "sister planet." How could two sisters be so unlike each other? We will examine that problem in the next chapter.

Mars: Planet of Life?

While Venus has been mysterious, Mars has been tantalizing. Ever since 1888, when the Italian astronomer Giovanni Schiaparelli (1835-1910) announced his discovery of the *canali,* astronomers have argued loudly and sometimes bitterly about the possibilities of life on Mars.

Percival Lowell spent the last half of his life and a considerable amount of his fortune trying to prove that Schiaparelli's *canali* were actually canals built by intelligent Martians. The Italian word simply means "channels," and Schiaparelli himself only claimed that there were straight line markings on the face of the red planet. Some astronomers saw them, others did not. Lowell drew intricate maps of Martian canals that connected the white polar caps with the dark oases—obviously the work of intelligent engineers who were trying to bring water to their cities, he concluded. Other astronomers dismissed the whole business as nothing but an optical illusion.

But photographs of Mars taken from the largest optical telescopes occasionally showed faint straight line markings where Lowell and others insisted they had seen canals. The problem was that even the best and biggest telescopes on Earth could not see Mars very clearly. At its closest approach to Earth, Mars is some 56 million kilometers away. It presents a disk that is 70 times smaller than the Moon. Only the broadest, sharpest surface markings can be seen from Earth, even under the best seeing conditions. Thus Earthbound astronomers could see the Martian polar caps and dark oases set against the reddish deserts of Mars, but the existence of the canals was always debatable.

Earthbound measurements showed that Mars is very cold and dry. Although midsummer temperatures may climb as high as 300°K (about 70°F) during the afternoon along the Martian equator, by nightfall the temperature at the same spot is below freezing, and by midnight it is often more than 100° below freezing.

Mars has an atmosphere, but a very thin one. Second Era astronomical estimates placed the density of Mars' atmosphere somewhere around 1/10 of Earth's. This was 10 times too high, as we will soon see.

But there is the "wave of darkening" in the Martian spring, when the polar cap melts and the oases go from gray to a darker color that has sometimes been described as blue-green (it is very difficult to pin down exact shades of color under the conditions in which the Martian oases are observed).

Since Mars could come no closer to Earth, the Mariner 4 spacecraft carried man's curiosity to Mars. On July 14, 1965, Mariner 4 passed within 10,000 kilometers of the red planet. On board the spacecraft were six scientific instruments and a television camera.

Mariner 4 telemetered 22 photographs of Mars back to the eager scientists of Earth. The pictures showed no canals. But they staggered the astronomical world with a complete surprise: Mars is pitted with craters, very much as the Moon is. No one had expected this. (Well, hardly anyone. Actually, writer George W. Harper predicted a crater pitted Mars in a thoughtful article in *Analog Science Fact and Fiction Magazine* in May, 1963.)

The other instruments on Mariner 4 measured cosmic radiation, the solar wind, and cosmic dust between Earth and Mars. There was also a magnetometer aboard to search for signs of a Martian magnetosphere. No magnetic field was detected, and no belts of trapped particles were found. The measurements showed that if Mars has any magnetic field at all, it must be less than 1/1000 of Earth's magnetic field strength.

The lack of a magnetosphere tells us something about the chances for life on Mars. On Earth, our magnetosphere shields us from most of the energetic particles streaming in from the Sun and beyond. Only the strongest cosmic particles plough through our "magnetic umbrella" and these are usually stopped by the atmosphere. On Mars, with no magnetosphere and only a whisp of atmosphere, solar wind particles, cosmic particles, and high energy ultraviolet and gamma rays must reach the surface constantly.

While the photographs from Mars were the most striking pieces of data to come from the Mariner 4 mission, the spacecraft performed a rather daring maneuver that allowed scientists to make precise measurements of the Martian atmosphere. The NASA engineers programmed Mariner 4's trajectory so that it would fly behind Mars, and be occulted by the planet. This was a courageous decision for them to make, because radio contact would be cut off once the spacecraft disappeared behind the planet. No one could guarantee that radio contact would be reestablished after the spacecraft reappeared on Mars' other side. If contact was not reestablished, all of the mission's data, including the photographs, would be lost.

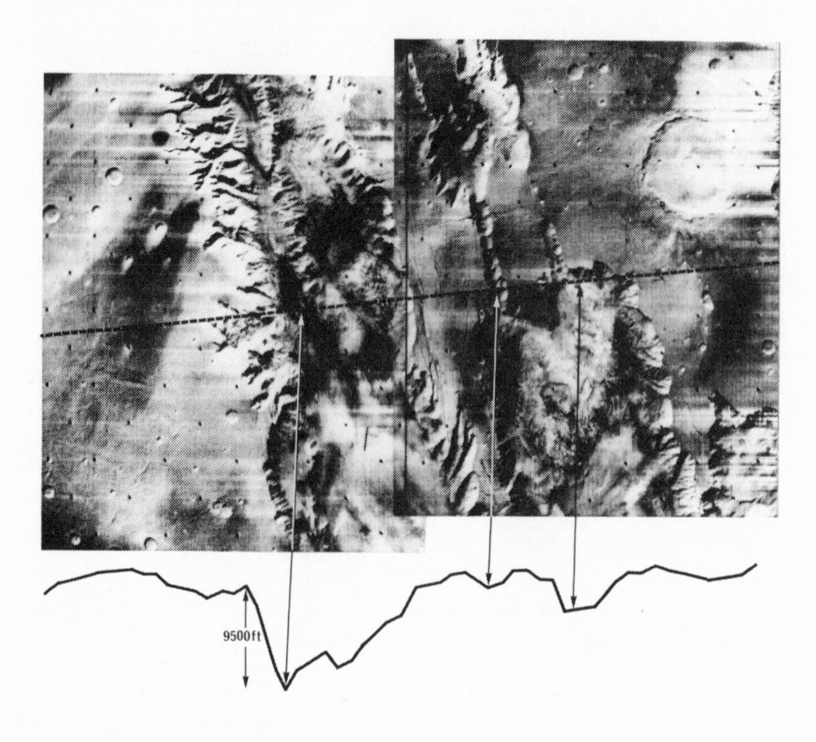

Fig. 7-6. Mariner 9 photo shows a seemingly eroded canyon on Mars that is longer and deeper than Grand Canyon. Before Mariner 9, Mars was thought to be a "dead," inactive planet. But evidence for volcanoes and erosion have forced scientists to revise their opinions of the Red Planet. (NASA)

Remember, Mariner 4 was the first spacecraft to be sent to Mars by the United States. Two years earlier, the Russian spacecraft Mars 1 had been lost when radio contact broke down some 106 million kilometers from Earth. America's Mariner 3 had been launched at Mars some three weeks before Mariner 4, but failed in flight very shortly after lift off.

So despite the risks, the occultation experiment was agreed upon. It was too good an idea to turn down—if it worked. The idea was that as the spacecraft went behind Mars its radio signal would pass through the Martian atmosphere before being blocked off by the solid body of the planet itself. By studying the way in which the radio signal was distorted, the Earthbound scientists and engineers could determine many details about the composition and structure of the Martian atmosphere.

Mariner 4 sailed behind Mars on the daylight side, where the local time was early afternoon; 54 agonizing minutes later it came out at a region where it was local midnight. The radio contact was regained immediately, and several hundred NASA engineers and astronomers started breathing again.

The distortions of the radio signal showed that Mars' atmosphere has a surface pressure that is only 1/200 of Earth's sea level atmospheric pressure. This is equivalent to the atmospheric pressure at about 40 kilometers altitude on Earth, high in our stratosphere. Mars has an ionosphere, a layer of charged particles about 100 kilometers above the surface.

The occultation experiment led astronomers to the conclusion that Mars' atmosphere must be composed almost entirely of carbon dioxide. But this is an estimate based on indirect evidence, and is subject to change as better information becomes available.

The temperature inferred for the Martian surface by the Mariner 4 instruments was about 160°K (-170°F) on the average, far colder than the lowest temperature ever recorded on Earth. This evaluation was made early in the Martian afternoon; nighttime temperatures go even lower.

Mariner 4 was a landmark in man's study of Mars. And by 1969, space flight technology had reached the point where two cooperative spacecraft could be launched toward the red planet for a joint mission.

While the first men were walking on the Moon, Mariners 6 and 7 were coasting toward Mars. They came to within 3500 kilometers of Mars and performed an intricate cooperative space ballet, taking photographs and making a variety of measurements, many of them in the infrared and ultraviolet.

Mariners 6 and 7 each had two television cameras, one with a wide angle lens and the other with a close up lens. Between them, they sent back to Earth a total of 202 pictures, taken in a range of 1.7 million kilometers to 3500 kilometers' distance.

The far distance photos "filled in" our previous views of Mars from the best observations ground based telescopes can make to the close up photographs such as those made by Mariner 4. New astronomers have a complete sequence of views, and can match the close up details of the Martian surface with the overall features of the entire planet.

The most spectacular feature of the "far encounter" photographs is the bright area known since the 19th century as Nix Olympica. It turned to be a single huge crater, some 500 kilometers across, larger than anything on the Moon.

The Mariner 6 and 7 cameras showed three distinct types of terrain on Mars.

There are vast stretches of territory that are pockmarked by more than 10,000 craters. These regions look very much like the Moon, although generally the Martian craters seem to be more eroded than the Moon's—smoother, and perhaps shallower. No doubt the thin Martian atmopshere has gradually worn them down, although this atmosphere might still be substantial enough to destroy incoming meteoric dust and prevent that type of erosion from working on Mars as it does on the Moon. If there is truly water vapor in the Martian atmosphere or liquid water underground, this may have helped to erode the craters.

Many of the Martian craters have flat, smooth bottoms. Some form of ice or frost has been seen in the bottoms of some of these craters. But it is not certain whether this frost is from water or frozen carbon dioxide (dry ice).

Other areas of Mars are entirely free of craters—most noticeably the large desert region called Hellas. How can this be? It is hard to believe that some 10,000 craters have speckled the surface of Mars but have stayed completely away from a region that is 1600 kilometers across. On the other hand, it is almost equally difficult to imagine some process that could have covered over such craters and left the terrain as smooth and featureless as Hellas appears to be.

Finally, there are regions on Mars that geologists call *chaotic*—wild, rugged regions of jumbled rock ridges and gorges. On Earth such "badlands" are caused by wind and rain erosion, and by flowing streams of water. On Mars, where the air is practically non-existent and there is no rain at all, it is difficult to understand what could have produced such landscapes.

The infrared and ultraviolet measurements made by the Mariner duo confirmed that Mars' atmosphere is almost pure carbon dioxide. The polar caps are apparently frozen carbon dioxide, rather than frozen water. There might be some water present at the caps, and there seems to be a trace of water vapor in the atmosphere. But there is far less water on the entire planet Mars than in the Great Lakes on Earth. This makes the chances for life such as our own seem quite slim.

None of the pictures of Mars has shown anything like a canal. The Mariner 6 and 7 photos did show that in a few of the areas where Lowell and others saw canals, there are scattered dark markings that might be linked up to form a straight line in the eyes of an observer some 150 million kilometers away.

The Mariner flights have shown no trace of life on Mars. But most satellite photographs of Earth, made at much closer distances than the Mariners achieved with Mars, do not show any signs of life on Earth! In the latter years of the 1970s, spacecraft will soft land on Mars and take samples of the air and soil for automated chemical and biological analyses. There are apparently no intelligent Martian canal builders, but there might still be life on Mars, as we will see in the next chapter.

During November and December 1971 three unmanned spacecraft—America's Mariner 9 and Russia's Mars 2 and 3—took up orbits around Mars, the first time astronautics engineers ever tried to place spacecraft in orbit around another planet. On December 2, 1971, a landing capsule from Mars 3 touched down in the area of Hellas, on the southern Martian continent.

These three spacecraft arrived at Mars during a planet-wide dust storm, that had been predicted by several astronomers who had studied Martian weather patterns. Millions of people all over the world were at first disappointed because the earliest television pictures from the orbiting spacecraft showed little more than a blanket of featureless dust, but the astronomers were actually delighted. They realized that they'd have a chance to see how Mars is changed by such a titanic storm, once the dust settled down. Since the spacecraft were orbiters, rather than one-shot flyby types, they were still in orbit and transmitting high-quality pictures and other data after the storm died away.

The Russian Mars 3 lander plunged to the surface while the storm was still raging. Slowed by a combination of retro-rockets and parachutes, it reached the surface and transmitted data—but only for 20 seconds. Since winds of more than 100 kilometers per hour might well have been howling at the surface during that time, it's possible that the lander was simply bowled over and damaged so much that its radio transmitter was knocked out of action.

But if the lander was a disappointment, the orbiters certainly were not.

The Mariner 9 instruments, which included infrared, ultraviolet and radio sensors as well as TV cameras, showed very clearly that the planet-wide dust storm affected not only Mars' surface, but its atmosphere as well. Temperature and the altitude and intensity of Mars' ionosphere of electrified particles were both significantly higher than they had been when measured two years earlier by the Mariner 6 and 7 spacecraft. Mascons—concentrations of heavy materials similar to those found under the lunar maria—were detected on Mars. Evidence of volcanoes and perhaps even ancient rivers were detected, as was some evidence for the possibility that water—frozen—was found at the polar regions. The south polar cap changed shape appreciably during the first week of Mariner 9's orbital surveillance, showing that either the cap is only a few centimeters thick and melts very quickly, or that its frozen crust was partially covered by dust from the storm.

The USSR's Mars 2 and 3 spacecraft also carried infrared, radio and television equipment. Details of their findings were not made available in time to be included in this book.

Touring the Other Planets

As this is being written, Mars and Venus are the only planets that we have reached with spacecraft. But plans are being made now for spacecraft that will go to Mercury and to the outer planets: Jupiter, Saturn, Uranus, Neptune and Pluto.

Between now and the end of the century, the outer planets will be in a series of alignments that will allow spacecraft to fly past two or more planets on a single, economical mission. Such "grand tours" could give us our first glimpses of the outer giant planets.

Life Forms in Meteorites

While our spacecraft exploration efforts have been sending men and machines out into the solar system, the constant infall of meteoroids that bombard the Earth has been bringing bits of the solar system to us.

As we have already seen, most of the meteoroids are microscopic dust grains, although some are much larger. A huge meteor blazed across the skies of Europe and Asia on June 30, 1908, and struck deep in a forest region of central Siberia, near the Tunguska River. It hit with the force of a nuclear bomb, knocking down trees for more than 30 kilometers in all directions. Another huge meteoroid caused the famous Barringer Meteor Crater in Arizona. And, of course, meteoroids have pockmarked the faces of the Moon and Mars, where there is little or no atmosphere to protect the surface.

When a meteoroid enters Earth's atmosphere, it usually burns up in the fiery glow of a "falling star." But occasionally intact meteoroids are found on the ground.

There are two basic types of meteorites: metallic and stony. The metallic meteorites are mostly iron and nickel. We will be more concerned here with the stony type: in particular, a kind of meteorite that is called *carbonaceous chondrite.*

Chondrites, or chondritic meteorites, are made up of small spherical bodies, called chondrules. Chondrules do not form under ordinary terrestrial conditions; apparently they are created under weightless conditions in interplanetary space. It appears most likely that the chondrules were once individual bits of stony, perhaps molten material that cooled and condensed into their present spherical forms. Then they gradually came together in space to build up larger bodies. This might be the way all the solid bodies of the solar system were built up, in a process called *aggregation:* tiny chondrules congregating together, perhaps attracted to each other by gravitational influences.

In a body as small as a minor meteoroid, the chondritic shapes can still be seen in the internal structure. But in planet-sized bodies, such as our Earth, the chondrules that originally formed it must be squeezed, deformed, even melted by heat and pressure, until they are no longer recognizable.

The carbonaceous chondrites are a particular form of chrondritic meteorite. They have an unusually high content of carbon in their makeup. This had been known for years, but not much attention was paid to the carbonaceous chondrites until 1952, when it was shown that they are also rich in oxygen, nitrogen, sulfur, hydrogen, chlorine and even water that is linked to the stone chemically in the form of hydrates.

In 1959 Melvin Calvin (born 1911) of the University of California announced the discovery of very complex substances in a carbonaceous chondrite—organic chemicals, the type which on Earth come only from living organisms.

Calvin had been studying the origins of life on Earth. This led him to a detailed examination of the process of photosynthesis, the process by which green plants create foodstuffs out of inert chemicals and sunshine. In 1961, Calvin received the Nobel Prize in chemistry for this work.

His interest in the origin of life led him to study the carbonaceous chondrites. He analyzed a sample from the Murray Meteorite, which fell in Murray, Kentucky, in 1950. The Murray chondrite was already somewhat notorious because it was the first meteorite ever known to hit a human being when it landed. It crashed through the roof of a house near Murray and grazed the woman who lived there.

Calvin was interested in the Murray chondrite because it was fairly fresh and had been handed over to scientists within a few days after it had landed. Thus there was comparatively little chance that it had been contaminated by Earthly chemicals or organisms. The discovery of organic chemicals in the Murray Meteorite was accepted by most scientists as evidence that complex chemicals can be built up in a meteorite—neither Calvin nor anyone else suggested that there were or had been living organisms in the meteorite.

But in 1961 a team of chemists led by Bartholomew Nagy, who was then with the Esso Research Laboratories, reported that they had found the remains of once living organisms inside two carbonaceous chondrites: the Orgueil Meteorite, which had fallen in southern France in 1864; and the Ivuna Meteorite, which had fallen in Tanganyika in 1938.

The scientific world seethed with an intense battle over Nagy's claims. Most researchers believed that, at best, Nagy and his colleagues had found spores of earthly origin that had "invaded" the meteorites over the years they had lain on dusty museum shelves. Nagy argued back that the forms he found resembled no known Earthy spores.

Despite Nagy's insistence, however, most of the scientists refused to believe that the chondrites actually carried the remains of organisms that were once alive: the consensus was that the meteorites had become contaminated with earthly organisms—until December, 1970.

A group of researchers at the NASA Ames Research Center in California reopened the entire question. Led by Indian born Cyril Ponnamperuma (born 1923), the NASA reasearch team examined a carbonaceous chondrite that had fallen near Murchison, Australia, on September 28, 1969. They found evidence of amino acids in the Murchison Meteorite. Amino acids are not merely organic chemicals; they are the basic building blocks for all animal life on Earth. Proteins are made of amino acids. All the different kinds of protein on Earth are built up of different combinations of just 20 fundamental amino acids.

Some of the amino acids found in the Murchison Meteorite closely match the amino acids found in terrestrial organisms (including us!). But others are unlike any amino acids existing on Earth today.

Are there life forms in the meteoroids? Or do these little chunks of rock and metal merely possess a share of complex chemicals—the types of chemical from which life springs, to be sure, but not living organisms themselves?

The meteorites come from two possible sources in the solar system: the asteroid belt, or the heads of comets that have broken apart. Was there a planet once between Mars and Jupiter that broke apart to form the asteroid belt? Did this planet harbor living creatures? Or is the asteroid belt an area where the building material for a small planet never managed to get together because of the gravitational interference of mighty Jupiter nearby? If the asteroids are preplanetary material, then they might be telling us, *via* meteorites, that the basic building blocks for life already exist in the building blocks of other planets.

What does this mean for the chances of finding life on other worlds?

It is time now to put together all the new ideas and information that have come from the new astronomies, and see how the solar system, and the universe beyond it, look to the scientists of the Third Era of astronomy.

8.

The New View of The Solar System

The general features of the solar system were discovered during astronomy's Second Era. The planets out to Pluto were identified, the source of the Sun's energy was determined, and the origin of the solar system was deduced—at least in broad outline. Now, with the aid of the new astronomies, we can "fill in the map" with more accurate detail, correct earlier mistakes, and add new ideas that have come out of astronomy's Third Era.

Origin of the Solar System

It seems clear that the entire solar system was created in a single, continuous process. The ages of the Earth, the Moon and of meteorites are all about the same. The Sun is estimated to be about the same age, too: 4.5 billion years old. However, the scarcity of solar neutrinos has led some astronomers seriously to question this estimate of the Sun's age.

The age of the Sun has been deduced from theoretical considera-

TABLE 8-1. MAJOR PLANETS OF THE SOLAR SYSTEM

Planet	*Avg. Distance from Sun* Millions of KM	AU	Diameter (km)	Density	Orbital Period	Period of Revolution
Mercury	58	0.39	4840	3.8	88 days	58.5 days
Venus	108	0.72	12,228	4.8	243 days	225 days
Earth	150	1.00	12,742	5.5	24 hrs	365.26 days
Mars	228	1.52	6770	3.9	24.5 hrs	687 days
Jupiter	778	5.20	140,720	1.3	10 hrs	11.8 yrs
Saturn	1428	9.54	116,820	0.7	10.5 hrs	29.6 yrs
Uranus	2872	19.14	47,100	1.5	10 hrs	88.7 yrs
Neptune	4498	30.20	44,600	2.5	12 hrs	166 yrs
Pluto	5910	39.44	6400 (?)	4.8 (?)	?	248 yrs

tions, plus spectroscopic evidence of the abundance of various elements in the solar plasma. The effective age of the Sun really can only be ascertained by measuring the ratio of hydrogen to helium deep in the Sun's interior, where spectroscopic examinations cannot be made.

Since the thermonuclear processes that make the Sun shine are conversions of hydrogen into helium, the more helium there is at the core, the older the Sun must be. But there is no way to measure the amount of helium deep inside the Sun. Instead, astrophysicists have made theoretical "models" of the Sun, based on its overall density, energy output, mass, observed hydrogen-helium ratio at the surface, et cetera. These models have generally worked out the estimate of 4.5 billion years. More important, perhaps, they indicate another 10 billion years or so of stable life ahead of it.

The neutrino experiments discussed earlier have cast some doubt on these models. Although the neutrinos are the only bits of material evidence we have that come straight from the Sun's interior, the difficulties and trickiness of the neutrino experiments have caused most astrophysicists to be very careful about embracing their results.

At present, then, most astronomers and cosmologists believe that the solar system is between 4.5 and 5 billion years old. It was formed out of a cloud of interstellar plasma—not gas—and cold dust grains. This plasma cloud was made almost entirely of hydrogen, but it also contained smatterings of heavier elements that had been "cooked" inside older stars and then spewed into space when these stars exploded. The cloud also contained a weak magnetic field.

We have seen such clouds in interstellar space; they are the *protostar* clouds that have been observed in regions such as the Orion Nebula, where many young stars have been found. A typical protostar cloud is about a lightyear in diameter.

Interestingly, these protostar clouds are the sites where radio telescopes have detected complex molecules. And we have seen that the protostars are strong infrared sources.

The cloud of interstellar plasma was moving and rotating. As it spun it began to shrink—any cloud of gas or plasma will tend to contract as it spins. The more it contracted, the faster it spun, which made the shrinking go faster, which increased the spin rate, and so on. The cloud literally fell in on itself, undergoing what astrophysicists call a *gravitational collapse*. This all took place in about 10 to 100 million years, an eyeblink in astronomical time scales.

The collapse would have ended with a fast spinning star surrounded by a cloud of gas and dust, if the original solar cloud had been gas. In fact, the solar system consists of a slow spinning star (the Sun rotates once in about a month) and a handful of solid bodies with a very thin ionized gas wafting outward from the sun. Most of the early theories of the solar system's origin fell apart on precisely this point. They could not posit a slow spinning sun with planets; their results were a fast spinning sun surrounded by a gas cloud that would quickly blow away into interstellar space.

But the original solar cloud was plasma, not gas. That made all the difference, as was pointed out by the Swedish physicist Hannes Alfven (born 1908), among others.

The original plasma cloud contained a magnetic field. As the cloud collapsed, the field intensified, concentrated into a constantly smaller volume of plasma. And the stronger the magnetic field became, the more important its role in shaping the solar system.

The central mass of plasma was on its way to becoming the Sun, and is often referred to at this stage as the *protosun*. In obedience to the laws of physics, the protosun wanted to spin faster and faster as it shrank. But the magnetic field prevented this. The magnetic field slowed the protosun's spin rate by transferring spin energy from the protosun to the swirling cloud of plasma and dust that surrounded the protosun. In this way, the magnetic field acted like the spokes of a wheel, transferring spin energy from the hub of the wheel, the protosun, out to the rim.

In all probability, the plasma cloud around the protosun actually flattened to a disk that stretched outward from the protosun's equator. Thus all the planets of the solar system, which formed out of that disk, are now in orbits that lie close to the Sun's equator. And the Sun rotates quite slowly. Its polar regions turn once every 34 days, while the equatorial region completes a revolution in about 25 days.

The flattened disk that hugged the protosun's equator extended outward for billions of kilometers. It was made of plasma, magnetized, and laced with dust grains. Out of it grew the planets and moons and asteroids and comets we know of today. Some of the dust is still there, as is the magnetic field.

The exact details of how the solid bodies were built up out of dust grains are still being debated. It seems obvious, though, that the dust grains coalesced to form chondrules, and the chondrules came together to form bigger and bigger bodies. This process is called *aggregation,* or *accretion;* it is believed to be responsible for the build up of all the solid bodies of the solar system.

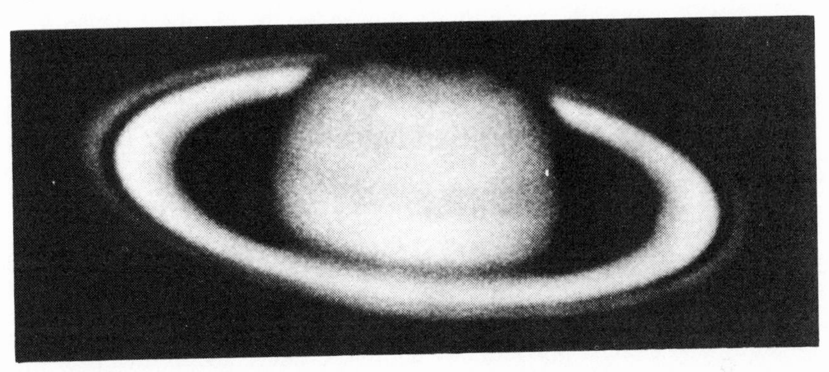

Fig. 8-1. The planet Saturn, with its beautiful rings. (Yerkes Observatory)

We have seen evidence for the accretion process in meteorites, which are still small enough to reveal their chondritic origin (although the metallic meteorites show a very different microscopic structure; presumably they were formed under great pressure).

As the protosun continued to condense, its interior density and temperature rose. It began to glow as the gravitational energy of its collapse was converted into heat. It became a strong infrared source, then gradually its energy output shifted predominantly into the visible wavelengths as its temperature continued to climb. Finally, when the interior temperature reached something like 20 million degrees, the hydrogen started to fuse into helium. The thermonuclear reactions produced a new energy source in the Sun. It became a true star. The collapse stopped, because the energy source created pressure forces inside the Sun that balanced out the gravitational force of collapse. For the past 4.5 billion years or so, the Sun has maintained a very stable output of energy, and stayed at its present size and shape.

The young planets that orbited the Sun were built out of the same solar material—mostly hydrogen and helium, with traces of heavier elements. But the planets closest to the Sun could not keep the very light elements for long, because their temperatures were too high. On Mercury, Venus, Earth and Mars almost all of the original free hydrogen and helium simply boiled away into space. The more distant Jupiter, Saturn, Uranus and Neptune were able to hold onto much of their original material, and are giant planets mainly because they are built from the more abundant hydrogen and helium.

Pluto is difficult to explain because it is so far away that not much has been learned about it. Pluto may once have been a satellite of Neptune's that somehow escaped to establish its own independent orbit. Its orbit crosses the orbit of Neptune. In fact, at present Neptune is actually the farthest planet of the solar system. Pluto crossed Neptune's orbit in 1969, and will not recross it until 2009.

There are still plenty of unanswered questions about the solar system's beginnings, particularly about the accretion build up of the planets. To explain the formation of the planets, it is necessary to assume that the disk of plasma around the protosun was from 10 to 100 times more massive than the combined masses of all the known solid bodies of the solar system today. Otherwise, the plasma disk would have been too thin to allow solid bodies to coalesce out of it. The plasma would have blown out into interstellar space and evaporated.

Where did this "extra" material go? One possible answer is that it was expelled from the solar system much as the solar wind is now wafting hydrogen plasma outward into deep space. But some cosmologists find this is much too convenient: the material was here when we needed it to build up the planets, and now it has very cooperatively gone away.

On the other hand, there are several pieces of observational evidence that support the basic theory of the solar system's origin out of a plasma cloud. For one thing, we have observed such protostar clouds in regions such as the Great Nebula of Orion, areas rich in young stars.

There is also circumstantial evidence for the magnetic braking idea. Astronomers have found that the youngest, hottest stars all are spinning quite fast; spin rates up to 500 kilometers per second are not uncommon. But stars of the Sun's age are all spinning at rates more like 5 kilometers per second. The conclusion drawn is that the young stars have not had enough time to allow their magnetic fields to slow them down, while the old stars have.

Does this mean that the older stars have planetary systems orbiting around them?

No astronomer has seen a planet of another star. Planets are simply too small and dim to be observed from Earth; the distances between the stars have defeated all attempts.

But astronomers *have* observed that a few of the stars closest to us are evidently accompanied by *unseen companions:* bodies that are too small and dim to be seen visually, but big enough to exert a noticeable gravitational pull on the star. Like any body in frictionless space, a star will move along a straight line path unless some outside force acts upon it. A few nearby stars—such as Barnard's Star, the second closest star to our solar system—show a measurable "wobble" as they move through space. There must be something unseen nearby that is pulling on the star with gravitational force. Calculations have shown that in each case, the "something" is about the mass and distance of a very large planet.

These unseen companions may not be planets at all, they may be miniature dark stars. Even if they are planets, they can hardly be expected to be Earth-like worlds. But of the 12 nearest stars, 3 of them are known to have unseen companions. Farther stars must have them, too, but their great distance prevents astronomers from detecting the slight wobble that such companions cause in the star's motion. However, 1/4 of the nearest 12 stars are accompanied by planet-sized bodies. Planetary systems may not be at all rare in the universe, which is a conclusion that we should expect, based on the idea that our own solar system formed as a completely natural sequence of events.

The Inner Planets

Mercury, Venus, Earth and Mars were once called the *terrestrial planets*. During the Second Era, it was convenient to think of these four inner planets of the solar system as being much like each other, and very much unlike the gas giant planets farther out from the sun.

With radio, radar, and spacecraft probes, the new astronomies have shown that these worlds are hardly like Earth. They are all comparatively small and dense, true enough. But there the similarities end.

Earth is the largest and densest of the inner planets. It is the only planet in the whole solar system that is at a temperature where liquid water can exist on the surface. And Earth is brim full of water. Moreover, it is the only planet we know of that harbors life—not only life, but intelligent life.

Living creatures have transformed this planet. Before life arose on Earth, our atmosphere was predominantly carbon dioxide, methane and ammonia. Green plants began using photosynthesis to turn carbon dioxide, water and sunshine into carbohydrate food. The plants took carbon dioxide from the air and released free oxygen. The oxygen attacked the ammonia and methane in the atmosphere, turning it into water vapor, carbon dioxide and free nitrogen.

Today we have an atmosphere of nitrogen and oxygen, with some water vapor, carbon dioxide, and inert gases. Green plants cover this world almost from pole to pole, and across the oceans (where they originated).

Our Earth would not be the way it is if life had not arisen here. Does the fact that the other planets are very unlike Earth mean that they do not bear life?

We know very little about the planet Mercury, actually. The fact that astronomers could erroneously assume for 3 generations the Mercury was in locked rotation around the Sun shows how shockingly little we know. Thanks to radar, we now have an accurate measure of Mercury's 58.5 day rotation. Infrared and radio measurements of Mercury's surface temperature show that it reaches a high of more than 600°K on the day side, and falls to a low of just about 273°K (the freezing point of water) at night. No atmosphere has been detected on Mercury, and calculations show that none should be expected. The planet is small, and hence has a low gravitational field strength. Its high daytime temperature means that gas molecules can reach speeds high enough to escape from the planet altogether. If Mercury originally had an atmosphere, it has long since boiled off into space. There is a chance that some heavy gases might still be clinging to the planet's surface, but no positive identification of such gases has been made.

Astronomers are trying to determine why Mercury rotates in 58.5 days. Is it on its way toward locked rotation, where it will indeed keep one side always facing the Sun? Or are there other gravitational influences that are preventing Mercury's rotation from "locking onto" the Sun?

The rotation of Venus is an even bigger headache to astronomers. As we saw in Chapter 5, Venus rotates backward, in the retrograde direction, opposite the rotation direction of every other planet in the solar system.

This anomaly profoundly disturbs astronomers. It is not that they are fussy; they simply find it hard to explain why the Sun and all other planets could revolve in one direction, and Venus in the other. If the solar system was created all at the same time, then Venus should have started out moving in the same direction as everything else. Something disturbed Venus, something powerful enough—or violent enough—to "flip" the planet's direction of rotation. The energy involved in reversing the spin of some 4.5 billion trillion tons of planet is staggering to contemplate (Venus' mass is approximately 4.5×10^{21} metric tons).

Some astronomers have postulated that Venus might have been struck by an immense meteoroid—a minor planet, or a comet, perhaps—and this reversed the planet's spin. Others have pointed out that Venus spins in such a manner that it always presents the same face toward Earth whenever the two planets are closest together. Has Earth's gravitational influence subtly changed Venus' rotation?

The first radio measurements of Venus' surface temperature

startled most astronomers so much that they refused to believe them. For centuries, Venus had been pictured in many ways: some thought it might be a world much like Earth under those clouds, others envisioned a lush jungle planet, or even a planet-wide ocean.

The microwave temperature reading, followed by the Mariner and Russian Venus spacecraft missions, destroyed all those romantic pictures. Venus is a red hot oven, hotter than Mercury ever gets, in fact. Russia's Venus 7 craft, which soft landed on the surface, showed a temperature of more than 700°K and atmospheric pressure of about 100 times the surface pressure on Earth.

No liquid water can exist on that surface. If there were any liquids there, they would probably be pools of molten metals. In an atmosphere so thick and heavy, there can be no winds as we know them on Earth, merely an inexorable sluggish surging more like the movement of ocean tides back and forth from the day side to the night side. Of course, it is unlikely that any visible sunlight penetrates to Venus' surface through that kilometers thick layer of perpetual clouds.

The clouds themselves contain some water vapor or droplets, and perhaps many other chemicals in the gas and liquid phases, as well. The clouds may be mostly hydrocarbons, oily droplets with a bit of water mixed in.

The atmosphere below the clouds is almost entirely carbon dioxide, which produces the fantastic greenhouse effect that leads to Venus' very high temperature. The reason that the high temperature surprised most astronomers is that if you calculate the amount of solar energy coming into the planet, and the amount reflected immediately by those bright clouds, you would arrive at a temperature that is not much different from Earth's. However, such a calculation omits the runaway greenhouse effect that is present in Venus' atmosphere. No one expected this, until the first microwave measurements were made.

Despite the vast differences in surface conditions and atmosphere, Venus is similar to us in some ways—size, density, and interior structure.

Radar probes have shown that Venus has mountain chains stretching across its surface. This has important implications about the planet's interior. Mountain building implies that there are forces active below ground. On Earth, mountain building is associated with volcanoes, with titanic motions of the planetary crust, and, ultimately, with the fact that our planet has a hot core. Does the presence of mountain chains on Venus imply that the planet has a molten core?

There are mountains on the Moon, true enough, and there are large differences in elevation on Mars' surface. But these features were apparently caused when the bodies were formed (or perhaps by meteoric impacts). Here on Earth, we know that mountain building is a dynamic, continuing process. The Himalayas, for instance, are still rising. The mountain chains on Venus may also be the result of dynamic forces stemming from a hot interior.

Does our "sister world" harbor life?

Certainly not on the surface, unless it is life of such a totally alien nature that we cannot even picture it to ourselves. But high in those clouds temperatures are more Earth-like, and there is liquid water, carbon dioxide, sunlight—and apparently hydrocarbons, which are organic molecules. Realizing that *organic,* in this sense, does not necessarily mean any connection with living organisms, we can still be hopeful that life might exist in the clouds of Venus.

Mars, in many ways, is the opposite of Venus. Where Venus is hot and covered by a thick cloudy atmosphere, Mars is cold and has only a wisp of an atmosphere.

Mars is the only planet whose surface can be seen clearly; all the others are either cloud covered or too small and distant to see well. Second Era astronomers drew elaborate maps of Mars, complete with romantic names for its deserts, oases, and canals.

The Mariner spacecraft have provided much more detailed and less fanciful pictures of Mars. The canals are illusions; the Martian surface is scarred by craters much as the Moon is, and even the polar caps appear to be frozen carbon dioxide—dry ice. Where men such as Percival Lowell envisioned intelligent Martian engineers who spanned their planet with canals, the cameras and instruments of the Third Era have shown Mars to be a bare little world, bathed in lethal radiation from the sun and cosmic particles, arid, frigid, desolate.

But lifeless? Perhaps not. Some of the infrared measurements made by Sinton and others can still be interpreted as showing the possibility of plant-like life on Mars. And those seasonal color changes of the "oases" might be further evidence of Martian life.

The other major new piece of information comes from the microwave observations that indicate there may be liquid water in the top few centimeters of the Martian soil (see Chapter 5). If this is true, then hopes for finding life on Mars go up to a new high.

As we have seen, the Mariner observations indicated that the Martian polar caps are frozen carbon dioxide. There is no trace of liquid water on Mars' surface, and calculations have shown that under the conditions of Mars' low gravity and atmospheric pressure, water in the liquid state on the surface would quickly evaporate and escape from the planet entirely.

If liquid water exists under the surface, however, then water based life similar to our own might exist on Mars. But the conditions that such life forms must face are rugged, to say the least.

We have seen that Mars is cold. Most of the planet is well below freezing all the time, except for a few hours during summer days. Night temperatures of 100° below freezing are commonplace. The atmosphere has no free oxygen near the surface, although that would not necessarily hinder plant life at all. The Martian atmosphere does contain carbon dioxide, but hardly anything else.

In laboratory experiments here on Earth, scientists have placed terrestrial plants and seedlings such as beans, cucumbers and cactii in *Mars jars*—containers that are kept under simulated conditions of the Martian surface. The plants sprouted and grew in an environment of bitter cold, no oxygen, and very low atmospheric pressure. The only thing the scientists had to do to keep the plants alive and healthy was to add water. If there is water under Mars' surface, earthly plants might be able to grow there. If our form of life can survive on Mars, why could there not be native life forms on Mars?

One possible pitfall in this chain of reasoning lies in the fact that Mars' pitifully thin atmosphere allows "hard" solar radiation and cosmic particles to reach the ground. Such intense ultraviolet, x-ray, gamma ray and cosmic particle fluxes would kill unprotected earthly organisms.

If there is any Martian life, though, it may have developed methods of defending against such deadly radiation, such as growing thick, protective coatings, or living entirely underground. A few centimeters of soil would give considerable protection against most of the radiation, and might even help to protect the Martian organisms against the frigid cold of the night.

To get back to the question of water: If liquid water does exist in the Martian soil, where does it come from and how does it get transported around the planet?

The Mariner data strongly indicate that the polar caps of Mars are frozen carbon dioxide. This does not rule out the possibility that frozen water could exist in the caps, together with the dry ice. On the other hand, the subsurface water might be coming from underground sources, such as springs and underground pools.

If the water comes from the polar caps, then it must be transported by the atmosphere, just as water vapor is carried in our own atmosphere. Traces of water vapor have been found in the Martian atmosphere, as have various types of clouds. Several astronomers have pointed out that the "wave of darkening" could be the result of water evaporating at the pole each spring and being carried through the atmosphere. Martian plant life, if we can use such a term, would somehow obtain the water from the atmosphere. There are species of plants on Earth that get most of their water from fog and dew droplets, rather than from rain or snow.

Not enough is known about the workings of the Martian atmosphere to tell if any of this is really possible. The Martian conditions of very low atmospheric pressure and extremely cold overnight temperatures must make weather on Mars very different from anything on Earth.

But it is instructive to compare Mars with our own Moon. Both are small worlds, and probably their bodies are now cold and inactive down to the very core. Both are pitted with thousands of craters. Yet they still look very different. The Moon is bare and apparently lifeless, even though some organic material might exist in its rocks. Mars has an atmosphere, polar caps, seasonal changes of color. Do these things mean that there is life on Mars? Perhaps not. But the chances are strong enough to warrant much closer investigation of the red planet. Probably not until spacecraft touch down on the Martian surface, and begin sampling the soil and air directly, will we start to get definite word on the existence of Martian life.

The Mystery of the Double Planet

The solar system has many mysteries, and one of the most intriguing is the existence of a double planet—two worlds that are so close together that one of them orbits around the other.

We are speaking of the Earth and the Moon. A double planet? Yes, because our Moon is not only one of the largest in the solar system, it is by far the largest in comparison to its primary planet.

Mars' moons are just tiny chunks of rock, a few kilometers in diameter. The largest moon in the solar system, Titan, is only 1/20 the size of its parent planet, Saturn. Yet our Moon is 1/4 the size of Earth.

How did we get such a Moon?

There are a number of theories. One claims that the Earth and the Moon were once a single body that split apart. Another is that the Moon was originally located elsewhere in the solar system and somehow came close enough to Earth for our planet to "capture" it. A third possibility is that the Earth and the Moon were originally created very close to each other—never physically connected, but never far separated either.

The evidence from the lunar rocks is tantalizing. The rocks of the Moon are very similar to terrestrial rocks, as we saw in Chapter 7. Yet there are significant differences. The Moon's crust is apparently made of basaltic rock, with lighter types of rock riding atop the basalt to form the mountainous highlands. This is similar to the structure of Earth's crust, with granitic continents riding atop heavier basalts.

The Moon's overall density is slightly more than 3 times the density of water, much lower than the Earth's density of 5.52. Therefore the Moon probably has no heavy iron core, as the Earth does. This has led some astronomers to the conclusion that the Moon might have been torn away from the Earth's crustal rocks, leaving a vast, gaping scar on the face of our planet: the Pacific Ocean.

No matter how the Moon was originally formed, or where, the evidence on its face shows that it has undergone a terrifically violent battering.

We can understand a crater pitted Mars, because Mars is close to the asteroid belt and has little atmosphere to protect it from stray chunks of rock and metal that fall into the grip of its gravitational field. The Moon has no atmosphere at all, and therefore is less protected than Mars. But the question is: where did the crater making meteoroids come from? The really huge craters, the lunar maria, are almost all on the side facing Earth. The far side of the Moon is remarkably free of maria. Why? And what made all those craters? Meteoroids from the asteroid belt? That seems unlikely. After all, the Moon is more heavily cratered than Mars, even though it is more than 50 million kilometers farther away from the asteroid belt.

We might also ask why Earth is not cratered like the Moon. The answer is in our atmosphere. Not only does our pleasantly thick air shield us from all but the biggest of meteoroids, but the wind and rain of our atmosphere weather and eventually erase even the largest craters on our world. The monster meteoroid that blasted our *Mare Imbrium* on the Moon would have been worn down to a smaller size if it had blazed into Earth's atmosphere. Still, when it hit the surface it would have made a city sized crater. Over eons of time, wind and weather would have smoothed out the crater rim and filled in its bowl.

Even so, geologists have found the remains of huge craters on our planet. They are called *astroblemes*: scars from the stars. And of course, younger craters, such as the famous Barringer Meteor Crater in Arizona, are still too fresh to have been weathered away.

It seems clear that billions of years ago both Earth and the Moon were bombarded by huge meteoroids. Chances are that these chunks of celestial bombshells were part of the original building material that formed the Earth and the Moon. We can picture a period very early in the solar system's history when the Earth and Moon formed out of the original clots of chondrules that surrounded the Sun. In the final agonies of our twin planets' creation, meteoroids the sizes of mountains must have slammed into the Earth and Moon time and again. Eventually, all this loose floating debris was swept away, pulled either into the Earth or to the Moon by gravity. The scars of this bombardment have been almost entirely wiped away by erosion on Earth. On the Moon, where the only erosive forces are due to micrometeorite "sandpapering," the craters are still very much in evidence.

The fact that the Moon is still very much in the same condition that it was 4 billion years ago has led astronomers to call our natural satellite "the solar system's museum of ancient history." Astronomers and selenologists are now studying that museum firsthand, thanks to the aid of the astronauts.

But the nagging question remains: How did a double planet get created? Why here, and nowhere else in the solar system?

The Mystery of the Double Star

While the Earth-Moon duo can be thought of as a double planet, our Sun and the planet Jupiter form a combination that comes close to being a double star.

Jupiter is by far the biggest of the planets, nearly 11 times the size of the Earth. But unlike the terrestrial planets, which are composed mainly of dense rocky and metallic elements, Jupiter is made of the lightest elements—hydrogen and helium, for the most part. This composition is much closer to the makeup of the Sun.

Optical studies of Jupiter, starting with Galileo's first telescopic observations, have revealed the planet's giant size and some information about its composition. Jupiter is covered with bands of varicolored clouds that swirl across its disk. The planet is rotating so fast—once in less than 10 hours—that it is noticeably flattened into an egg shape. The clouds contain ammonia (NH_3) and methane (CH_4), both compounds of hydrogen. Infrared observations have revealed the presence of molecular hydrogen (H_2), and theoretical considerations have led to the conclusion that there must be abundant helium in Jupiter's makeup as well.

The preponderance of light elements result in Jupiter's having a density only slightly above that of water: 1.34.

The gravitational field strength at the top of the visible cloud deck is 2.65 times stronger than Earth's surface gravity, and increases as you go in toward the center of the planet. The temperature at the cloud tops has been measured at 130°K (–225°F). Hardly star-like warmth!

And yet taking into consideration Jupiter's composition, gravitational field strength, mass, density, and temperature, it is possible to show mathematically that conditions deep inside the planet must approach the conditions inside a star. The hydrogen-helium material is squeezed into fantastic density at Jupiter's core, far denser than even the iron rich core of Earth.

Moreover, although Jupiter may appear quite cold by terrestrial standards, it is actually warmer than it "should" be. Jupiter is some 5.2 AU's from the Sun, and thus receives nearly 30 times less solar energy than we do. The clouds that cover Jupiter reflect about 45% of this incoming energy back toward space. (The term for this reflecting property is *albedo*. Jupiter's albedo is 0.45; brilliant Venus' is 0.76; Earth's is 0.39; the Moon's is a dim 0.07.)

Based on the amount of solar energy actually getting through the clouds, Jupiter's estimated temperature is around 105°K. But infrared measurements in the 8 to 12 micron region have shown that Jupiter has a temperature of 130°K. Why?

Many astronomers have concluded that Jupiter has some internal source of heat. It might be another sort of greenhouse effect, where incoming solar energy is trapped and drives the atmospheric temperature upward. Or it might be that there is actually some source of energy hidden deep inside those clouds. Jupiter may still be contracting slowly, squeezing in on itself and converting gravitational energy into heat. This is the way a protostar behaves.

Perhaps the solar system narrowly missed being a double star system! There are many binary star systems in the heavens: of the 37 stars within 5 parsecs of the Sun, 9 of them are actually binaries and 2 of them are triple star systems (including Alpha Centauri, the nearest star to our solar system). At least 4 of these stars have unseen dark companions that are presumably planets. The binary star 61 Cygni has a dark companion; the other 3 planetary possibilities are single stars.

But Jupiter simply does not have enough mass to turn into a star. Its central density and temperature will never become high enough to trigger nuclear fusion reactions.

Astronomers differ sharply about the possible conditions on Jupiter beneath the clouds. With the low temperature and ever increasing crush of gravity, it seems likely that the gases of Jupiter's atmosphere must become liquefied at some depth below the clouds. Further down toward the center of the planet the density must become high enough to solidify hydrogen itself into a metallic condition. Thus the chances are that Jupiter has a deep and corrosive atmosphere, a planet-wide ocean, and a metallic hydrogen core that is bigger than the whole Earth.

So Jupiter is hardly a terrestrial planet. The atmosphere is mainly molecular hydrogen and helium. The clouds contain considerable ammonia and methane, and probably many other chemical mixtures which have not yet been identified as well. Chemistry on Jupiter may be very different from anything we can recognize from our Earthly experience.

If there is a planet-wide ocean on Jupiter, it just might be made of water, if the planet is heated internally. After all, water is a very common substance: it is composed of two very abundant elements, and 2/3 of the water molecule, OH, has been found by radio telescopes in many interstellar clouds. Alternatively, Jupiter may have an ocean of liquid ammonia: clean, perhaps, but not inviting!

Although Jupiter does not sound much like home to us, the strange fact is that these conditions are quite similar to the conditions under which life first evolved on Earth. More than 2 billion years ago, Earth's atmosphere was rich in ammonia and methane. Only the actions of living organisms changed that atmosphere into the nitrogen-oxygen we have today. And life on Earth began in the sea.

On our planet, the energy that triggered life came from the Sun, and still does. On Jupiter, 5 times farther from the Sun and shrouded by thick clouds, the energy might come from internal sources, such as lightning discharges.

In 1960, two American scientists provided some experimental "evidence" that life might exist on Jupiter. Astronomer Carl Sagan (born 1934) and biochemist Stanley L. Miller (born 1930) put together a mixture of hydrogen, helium, ammonia and methane under the conditions assumed to exist below the Jovian clouds. Keeping the gas mixture at the low temperatures observed on Jupiter, they fired electrical discharges through it, to simulate the lightning that may be causing the flickering radio emissions from Jupiter.

The mixture produced simple organic compounds, carbon chain molecules such as those that form the backbone of living organisms on Earth. Sagan has concluded that if any planet in the solar system harbors life in addition to our own, it's probably Jupiter.

We saw in Chapter 5 that Jupiter has an extensive Van Allen belt and a strong magnetosphere. One of the mysteries about the planet is the strange behavior of its radio emission, which seems to be controlled in some unknown way by the position of its closest large Moon, Io.

But there are at least 2 other brain racking mysteries about Jupiter.

First there is the famous Red Spot, which is an oval shaped form that seems to hover in the Jovian cloud deck. It is nearly 50,000 kilometers long and more than 12,000 kilometers wide; 4 planets of Earth's size could nestle comfortably in the Red Spot!

No one has the faintest idea of what it is. The Red Spot drifts slightly in Jupiter's southern hemisphere while the clouds seem to swirl around it and rush past much faster. It looks like an island floating serenely in a sea of clouds. Can it be an island of sorts, perhaps made of particles? If so, why hasn't it broken up? And would the particles be the size of dust motes or icebergs? The Red Spot has been known since 1664, and has been observed continuously since the 1880s. Perhaps it *did* break up and reform during those two centuries: for long periods of time no one saw it. Since 1881 it has faded almost to invisibility, then darkened again to almost brick red.

Perhaps close investigation by spacecraft will unravel the Red Spot's mystery. Until then, we can only guess.

The second enigma goes back to Jupiter's relationship with the Sun.

When manned space flights first started, astronomers and astronautical engineers both realized that the radiation from solar flares poses a hazard to unprotected astronauts. Orbital flights within the

Earth's magnetosphere are no special problem, thanks to our planet's "magnetic umbrella." But flights to the Moon and beyond can run into dangerous radiation levels if a flare erupts during the mission.

For the Apollo flights to the Moon, therefore, attempts were made to predict the outbreak of solar flares—in essence, to forecast the weather on the Sun. To some extent these forecasts have been successful, and to date no lunar flight has been endangered by solar flares.

A few astronomers and engineers began to notice that there seems to be a striking relationship between the positions of the planets in their orbits around the Sun, and the occurance of strong sunspots and solar flares. When the planets are arranged around the Sun in certain patterns, sunspots seem to proliferate and solar flares become more frequent. When the planets arrange themselves in a different pattern, the Sun becomes quiet.

This smacks of astrology—predicting events by the positions of the planets! But it works well enough to convince some astronomers that there might be a physical reason for this relationship. They have now turned to Jupiter as the primary influence on the Sun's activity.

They point out that sunspot activity rises to a peak every 11 years, and Jupiter's orbit around the Sun is slightly more than 11 years.

Can there be some physical influence—subtle gravitational effects, perhaps—between the planets and the Sun that causes disturbances in the Sun's outer layers of plasma? If so, the influence is dominated by Jupiter, giant of the planets.

Filling in the Map

The outer planets of the solar system, beyond Jupiter, are less well known than those closer to us. Saturn has its beautiful and puzzling rings, of course. They are composed of ice chunks, and may be the remains of one or more moons that spun in too close to the planet and were broken up. Saturn, Uranus and Neptune are all gas giant planets, rather like Jupiter, but smaller and colder. Pluto is a blank: aside from its orbital path, hardly anything is known about this distant and seemingly small planet.

Our knowledge of the solar system is something like Henry Hudson's knowledge of the New World. We can draw a map that is fairly accurate as far as it goes, but there are enormous gaps in the map, areas of nearly complete ignorance.

In the years to come, as orbiting astronomical observatories become larger and more dependable, as deep ranging planet exploring spacecraft go to Mercury and make grand tours of the outer planets, we will start to fill in more and more of the blank spaces of our map.

These spacecraft will carry the instruments of the new astronomies of the Third Era. And eventually, they will carry men to Mars and beyond.

9.

The Violent Universe

The new astronomies have changed man's view of the universe, and have shattered earlier cosmological notions of how the universe began and how it will end.

By the end of the Second Era of astronomy, it was clear that the universe was a vast sea of space studded with galaxies, bright islands of stars in the dark emptiness. The most distant galaxies known were several billion parsecs (gigaparsecs) from the Milky Way. This universe of galaxies was expanding smoothly, as shown by the redshifts of the galaxies.

The origin of the universe, and the cause for its expansion, were simply explained. The universe started as a single unit, a *primeval atom* in the phrasing of the Belgian priest-cosmologist Georges Lemaitre (born 1894). This fantastically dense "egg" contained all the matter of the universe—all the stars and galaxies—in a sphere about 30 times larger than the Sun. The primeval atom exploded, leading eventually to the formation of the universe as we see it today. The expansion of the universe is a result of the explosion, which took place presumably some 10 billion years ago.

Lemaitre proposed this theory in 1931. In 1946 the Russian born American cosmologist and physicist George Gamow (1904-1968) brought a more detailed understanding of nuclear physics into the picture and improved Lemaitre's basic theory. Gamow nicknamed the concept the "Big Bang Theory".

The Big Bang Theory is *evolutionary* in nature. That is, it sees the universe as an entity that is evolving, changing with time. Once it was a dense primeval atom (or *ylem*, in Gamow's writings, pronounced EYE-lem). It exploded. Then galaxies and stars were created. The universe looks very different today than it did 5 or 10 billion years ago; 5 or 10 billion years from now it will look different from today. The universe is evolving.

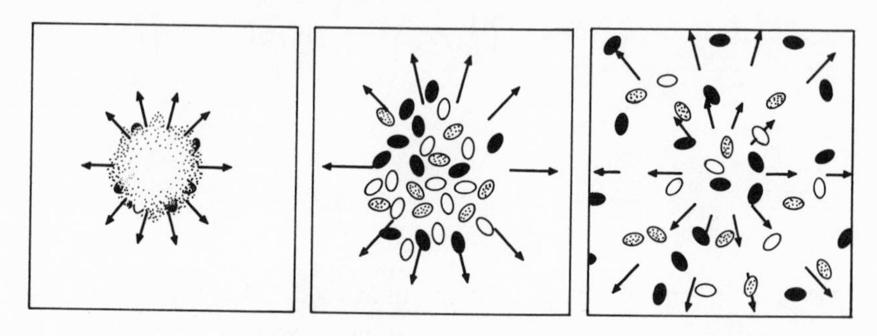

Fig. 9-1. If the universe originated in a Big Bang, the galaxies would be more closely clustered early in the universe's history (left) and get constantly farther scattered as the universe evolves (center and right). If the universe is in a Steady State, however, it will always look about the same as it does now (center) no matter how far into the past—i.e., how distant in space—we look.

In 1948, as the first radio telescopes of the Third Era were starting to make an impact on astronomy, a group of British cosmologists offered a startling different view of the universe and its origins.

Hermann Bondi, Thomas Gold, and Fred Hoyle (born 1919, 1920, and 1915, respectively) proposed the "Steady State Theory". In their view, the universe has no beginning and no end. Stars and galaxies are born, go through life cycles, and die out. They are replaced by new stars and galaxies, continuously. The universe looks the same today as it always did, or as it ever will. It is not an evolving universe, they say.

According to this Steady State Theory the expansion of the universe, as deduced from the redshifts, is caused by the continuous creation of matter. Matter is created, cause unknown, on an atom by atom basis, continuously. Instead of a primeval atom, we have matter continuously appearing in the universe, out of nothing.

The idea of the continuous creation of matter out of nothing was ludicrous to most astronomers and cosmologists, even though no one had ever tried to explain where the primeval atom came from. Despite loud arguments against it (or maybe because of the resultant interest) the Steady State Theory quickly became a challenger to the Big Bang Theory.

There was a simple way to decide which of the two theories was nearer the truth. As we look deeper and deeper into space, we see galaxies as they existed farther and farther ago in time. It takes light a finite amount of time to travel the vast distances between the galaxies. From the most distant galaxies, observed by the 200″ telescope at Mt. Palomar, we are receiving light that took billions of years to reach us. Thus we are seeing those galaxies as they existed billions of years ago.

If the evolutionary Big Bang Theory is correct, then the galaxies should be clustered together more densely at these vast distances, since the expansion of the universe from its primeval atom had not proceeded so far billions of years ago. If the Steady State Theory is correct, the galaxies will be sprinkled through space at about the same density no matter at which time or place they are seen.

Through the 1950s, astronomers attempted to measure changes in the density of galaxies over distances of gigaparsecs. The differences were so slight, and the measurements so delicate, that it was impossible to say definitely which theory was correct.

And then the quasars were discovered.

The Quasars

We saw in Chapter 5 that the quasars were originally detected because of their strong radio emission in 1960. By 1963, it was clear that these enigmatic quasistellar objects were neither stars nor ordinary galaxies. Their enormous redshifts—some of them are apparently moving away from us at 90% of lightspeed—place them out at the farthest edges of the known universe, twice as far as any true galaxy.

Considering their optical and radio energy outputs, and their distances as deduced from their redshifts, the quasars are emitting as much energy as 1000 Milky Way galaxies. They are among the strongest radio sources in the sky. They are also emitting strongly in the infrared and ultraviolet regions of the spectrum. A typical quasar is putting out as much energy as *10 billion* supernova explosions. Where does this fantastic energy come from? And how can it be packaged into a body that is much smaller than a galaxy?

So far in this chapter, we have assumed that the quasars are "cosmologically" distant—billions of parsecs away from us, out at the edges of the observable universe. This assumption is made because of their huge redshifts.

The redshift method for gauging cosmic distances is at best very rough, and depends on an interlinking chain of assumptions: 1: the observed redshifts are Doppler shifts, caused by the object's rushing away from us; 2: the reason the object is moving away is that the entire universe is expanding uniformly, so that the farther away a galaxy or quasar is from us the faster it is receding; therefore 3: the larger the redshift, the faster the object is receding, and thus the greater its distance from us.

Hubble showed in 1929 that if you make a graph in which you plot the brightness of the galaxies against their redshifts, the data falls on a beautiful straight line. This is powerful evidence that the redshifts are truly related to distance. For galaxies.

But if you plot the brightnesses of the known quasars against their redshifts, you do not get a straight line at all. You get a wild shotgun pattern, with no apparent relationship to anything except confusion.

This led Hoyle, one of the fathers of the Steady State Theory, to begin wondering if the quasars' redshifts might be completely unrelated to distance. Maybe the quasars are not cosmologically distant after all but relatively nearby, perhaps "only" a few million parsecs away.

Hoyle needed "local" quasars to save the Steady State Theory from attack. For if the quasars are truly cosmologically distant, they tend to show that the universe was definitely very different some 10 billion years ago than it is today. If you count the most distant galaxies and quasars together, they show a universe that was more densely packed with such objects in the primeval past. All this hurts the Steady State Theory, which claims the universe has always been about the same as it is today.

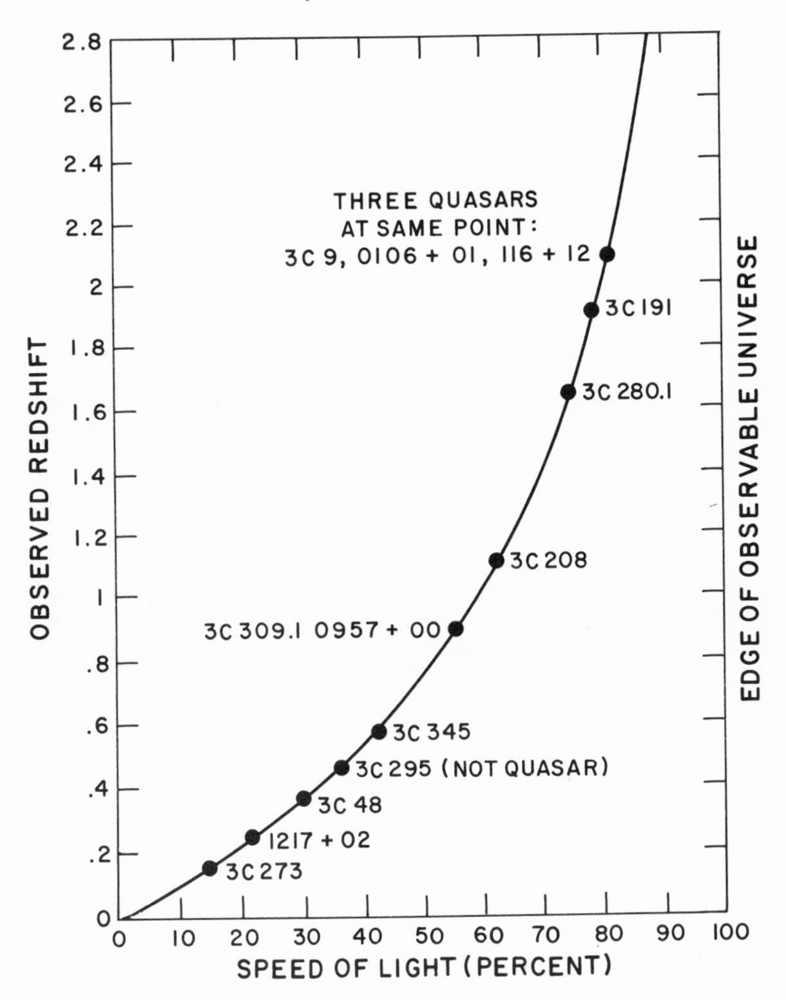

Fig. 9-2. Redshifts of several quasars and the farthest known galaxy (3C 295). Recent observations have found several quasars moving at about 90 percent lightspeed.

Moreover, some Big Bang enthusiasts were claiming that the quasars themselves were evidence of primeval bursts of energy—cataclysmic explosions that marked the beginnings of the universe.

However, if Hoyle could show that the quasars are local objects, the attack on the Steady State Theory is blunted. Moreover, if it could be shown that the redshifts of the quasars have nothing to do with their distances, then some doubt is cast upon the entire concept of judging cosmological distances by redshifts. This could even affect the very idea of an expanding universe.

Thus the argument between local and cosmological distances for the quasars has powerful emotional and intellectual forces at each end.

Superstars

In 1963 Hoyle and William Fowler (born 1911) of the California Institute of Technology, proposed that the quasars might be supermassive objects relatively close to our own galaxy. They pictured the quasars as being much smaller than a galaxy, perhaps the size of a globular star cluster. But where a globular cluster might contain 100,000 or even a million stars, Hoyle and Fowler saw the typical quasar as 100 million times the mass of the Sun. For lack of a better tag, their description of a quasar was called a *superstar*.

By "bringing in" the quasars from gigaparsecs to a few parsecs' distance, we lower the amount of energy that needs to be explained. At their observed brightnesses, local quasars would be emitting slightly less energy than a single galaxy; at cosmological distances, the same brightness equates to a thousand galaxies, as we have already noted.

Both the energy output and the redshift of the Hoyle-Fowler superstar comes from gravity. With a mass of 100 million suns, the superstar is collapsing in on itself, and converting gravitational energy into electromagnetic energy which is radiated away into space.

The titanic gravitational field of this supermassive object also causes the redshift. Photons of light emitted by the superstar must struggle against the gravitational field to get away from the superstar.

They must do work, fight their way "uphill." This causes them to lose some energy, which in turn causes a shift of their wavelength toward the red end of the spectrum. Calculations have shown that photons coming from our Sun are slightly shifted toward the red; the shift is too small to cause any practical consequences, in the case of the Sun. But for a superstar of 100 million solar masses, the gravitational field can cause the kind of redshifts that have been observed in the quasars.

The superstar idea came under attack as soon as it was announced. (*All* theories attempting to explain the quasars have been attacked from one quarter or another.) Physicists pointed out that a single object of 100 million solar masses could not remain stable; it would break apart. The theory's backers countered with the argument that the supermassive object need not be a single body: it could be a superstar cluster. They also presented some mathematical evidence to show that if the superstar rotated rapidly enough it would not break up.

The puzzle of the quasars, and the arguments over superstars, still rage on. Big Bang cosmologists want the quasars to be cosmologically distant. Steady State people want them local. In all fairness, there are just about as many proposed explanations for the quasars as there are astronomers. Several of the explanations call for local quasars.

For example, James Terrell (born 1923) of the University of California proposed in 1964 that the quasars might be something like massive star clusters that have somehow been "shot" out of our own or nearby galaxies. Their redshifts, then, would be Doppler shifts—but caused by their ejection from the galaxies, not by the expansion of the universe.

That same year, C. R. Lynds (born 1928) of the Lick Observatory and Alan Sandage (born 1926) of the California Institute of Technology showed that the relatively near galaxy M-82 is in the throes of a stupendous explosion. Its core has blasted itself apart, hurling immense filaments of hydrogen plasma more than 5000 parsecs outward from the center of the galaxy. Could the quasars be a sort of "shrapnel" fired out of exploding galaxies?

Gravitational Collapse

The embarassing problem of trying to explain the quasars with exploding galaxies is simply that a galactic explosion requires just about as much energy as a cosmologically distant quasar. So bringing the quasars in to local distances does not settle the baffling question of energy sources. Quasar or exploding galaxies—where does the energy come from?

Increasingly, astrophysicists have been thinking in terms of gravitational collapse as an energy source.

The idea that the quasars might be powered by gravitational collapse was not restricted to the backers of the local, superstar theory. Even those who believe that the quasars are cosmologically distant have considered gravitational energy as the driving force behind the fantastic outpouring of energy coming from the quasars. In this case, though, the quasar is envisioned as being about the size of a galaxy, and collapsing inward on itself. The energy release could be purely gravitational in origin, or it could come from the collision and explosion of billions of stars in the galaxy's core as they are squeezed together in the collapse.

The discovery of the quasars, and the realization that many radio galaxies have tiny regions in their cores where most of the radio emission comes from, led astronomers to start paying more attention to the central regions of galaxies. As we saw in Chapter 6, both infrared and ultraviolet observations have confirmed that the core of the Milky Way galaxy is much more active than had been suspected, although the total amount of energy emanating from the Milky Way's core is much lower than the emissions from such "active" galaxies as M-82 and M-87. Other galaxies—even radio quiet galaxies such as the Milky Way—have also revealed considerable agitation in their central regions.

This new interest in galactic cores recalled the work done in the 1940s by the American astronomer C. K. Seyfert (1911-1960), who studied a number of galaxies that have unusually bright cores. Seyfert galaxies, as they are now called, have very active central regions in which there is much loose gas that is highly excited and moving with velocities of some 4500 kilometers per second. While Seyfert worked

Fig. 9-3. A Seyfert galaxy, NGC 1275, which has a very bright and radio-emitting core. Seyfert galaxies somewhat resemble quasars, with active and fluctuating visible and radio core emissions. (Mt. Wilson and Palomar Observatories)

exclusively with optical telescopes, more recent radio studies of the Seyfert galaxies show them to be fairly powerful radio sources, with the radio emission coming from those bright, agitated cores. In many respects the Seyfert galaxies resemble the quasars, including the fact that both types of object tend to show sizable variations in light and radio output. But the quasars are at least a thousand times more energetic—if they are truly cosmologically distant.

By the mid-1960s, evidence for galactic explosions was pouring in on the astronomers. Lynds and Sandage showed that M-82 is exploding. Short exposure photographs of the elliptical galaxy M-87 revealed its optically bright core and the 10,000 parsec long jet streaking out from it. The Seyfert galaxies looked like the result of core explosions, and many thinkers were considering the idea that the quasars were very distant, very powerful galactic explosions—possibly results of the gravitational collapse of the galaxy.

The so-called double radio sources—galaxies that have two optically invisible but radio intense regions off to either side of them—also give the appearance of having thrown off these radio emission regions as the result of an explosion. There is even a chance that our own Milky Way galaxy suffered a core explosion at least a million years ago. The "halo" of radio emitting gases that surrounds the Milky Way could have been ejected from the core in an explosion that was similar, although perhaps less violent, than the one emitted by M-82.

What causes galactic explosions? Where does the energy come from? Is it a coincidence that the energy involved in an exploding galaxy, according to most calculations, works out to be very similar to the energy output of the quasars?

As in the case of the quasars, theoretical explanations for galactic explosions abound. Again, most of the possible explanations involve gravitational collapse in one form or another. Just what causes a galaxy to collapse is much less clear. As in all gravitational collapse phenomena, the outward pushing forces that counterbalance gravity somehow fail, and ever present gravity pulls the body together. But the outward pushing forces that hold a galaxy to its shape are only vaguely understood. Nor do astronomers understand why some galaxies are spirals, others elliptical, and still others rather formless. But when these forces—whatever they are—falter, the gravitational forces invested in billions of stars certainly have the energy to force the galaxy into a rapid contraction: a collapse.

A galactic explosion can be triggered by a gravitational collapse of the galaxy which leads to collisions of stars, or chains of supernova explosions, or—strangest of all—anti-matter explosions.

Anti-matter was first suggested by theoretical physicists such as P. A. M. Dirac (born 1902). In 1931, he proposed that there could exist a form of matter that was opposite in electrical nature to normal matter. The following year, experimental physicists produced and identified anti-electrons. The anti-electron is exactly like a normal electron, except that its electrical charge is positive, where the electron's charge is negative. For this reason, the anti-electron is known as the *positron*. In the following years, anti-particles were found for every type of atomic particle known: anti-protons, anti-neutrons, anti-mesons, even anti-neutrinos.

When a particle of anti-matter hits a particle of ordinary matter, they destroy each other in a flash of electromagnetic radiation. They are totally annihilated, and totally converted to energy. Fortunately, anti-matter does not exist naturally on Earth. It has been created in physics labs for fleeting fractions of a second. Nor does it seem to exist in the solar system: meteorites and lunar rocks do not annihihilate themselves when they touch Earthly material.

But what about out in deep space, among the stars? Or in other galaxies? Remember, when matter and anti-matter meet, they convert their entire mass into energy; the most energetic nuclear reactions in the solar system—the Sun's thermonuclear fusion—convert only 0.7% of the original hydrogen's mass into helium.

Matter/anti-matter annihilation may be an energy source for the quasars and the exploding galaxies, if anti-matter exists among the galaxies. And gravitational collapse may be the agent that forces matter and anti-matter into contact. If anti-matter exists in a galaxy that also contains normal matter, the two may meet—violently—when the galaxy collapses and both types of matter are squeezed together.

The Death of the Sun

The new found interest in gravitational collapse turned astrophysicists to rethinking how gravitational forces shape the life history of individual stars, as well as galaxies.

Stars begin their lives with a gravitational collapse, as we have already seen. A protostar contracts out of a cloud of plasma and dust that was originally perhaps a lightyear or more in diameter.

In the case of our Sun, why did its gravitational collapse stop when it did, leaving the Sun at its present almost perfectly spherical

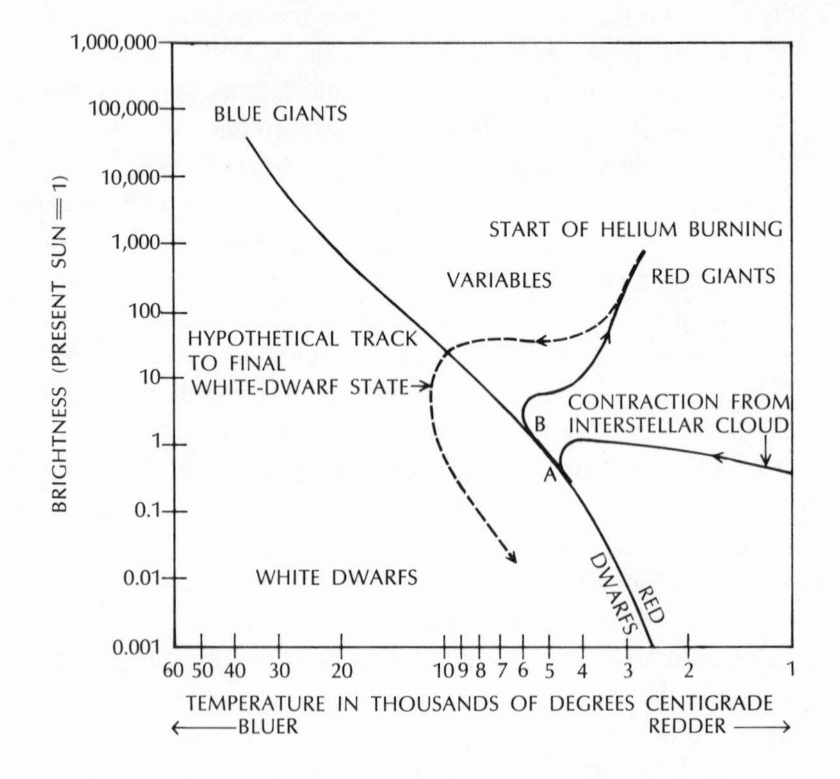

Fig. 9-4. Evolutionary track for a Sun-like star. The star begins in the contraction of a gas/dust cloud, becomes a stable Main Sequence star, then eventually evolves into a Red Giant and finally a White Dwarf star, as its nuclear fuel supplies run out.

diameter of 1.39 million kilometers? Why didn't the Sun become still smaller? The reason is that there are strong pressure forces pushing outward from the core of the sun, thanks to the 20 million degree fusion reactions going on in its core. These outward pushing pressure forces balance the inward pull of gravity.

In another 5 or 10 billion years, the Sun's supply of hydrogen will start to run low. Most of its core will be helium, the "ash" created by hydrogen fusion. The core will thus be denser than it is now, and therefore hotter. When its central temperature rises to some 100 million degrees, the helium will begin to undergo fusion reactions, creating carbon, oxygen and neon.

Because the core temperature will be higher, gravity will have to yield somewhat to increased pressure. The Sun's outer layers of plasma will expand. The photosphere will become distended and actually get cooler, since it will be farther away from the heat source at the core. The Sun's appearance will change: it will become larger, and its color will shift from yellow to orange and then red. The sun will become a red giant star.

When the helium in the core gets depleted, the oxygen, carbon and neon will begin fusing, at still higher temperatures, to form heavier elements. The same routine repeats over and again. The temperature of the sun's core will be constantly rising at this point, constantly producing heavier and still heavier elements.

Each cycle of heavier element building will go faster than the previous one; each cycle will bring the Sun closer to disaster. Through it all, gravity will be constantly outfought by the outward pushing pressure forces, and the Sun's outer layers will become hugely distended.

Until—the fusion reactions at the core produce iron.

When iron nucleii fuse together they produce lighter elements, not heavier ones. The game will be over. The Sun will have run out of new energy sources. Gravity, which will have been exerting pressure all along, will become the winner. The remainder of the Sun's life will depend more on the ever abiding force of gravity than on any other factor.

What will happen then?

Since 1915, when the first white dwarf star was discovered,

astronomers and astrophysicists have assumed that somehow most stars must eventually end up as dying white dwarfs. The first white dwarf identified by astronomers, incidentally, is the companion of Sirius, brightest star in our skies. Since Sirius is called the Dog Star, because it is part of the constellation of the Big Dog, its dwarf companion is often called the Pup.

How does a star go from being a red giant to a white dwarf? The question sounds more fitting for a fairy tale than for astrophysics. What role do stellar explosions play in these latter stages of a star's lifespan? Stars suffer nova and supernova explosions, as we have seen. A nova merely blows off a fraction of the star's outer layers; a supernova can wreck the star and release as much energy in 24 hours as the Sun emits over a million years. Will the Sun explode? If so, how violent will the explosion be?

Recent work on gravitational collapse has helped to show what happens to stars as they reach the end of their lives.

For a star of the Sun's mass, the story seems straightforward. Once outward pushing pressure forces can no longer support the star's size, gravity begins to compress the star. The Sun will begin to fall in on itself. As the gravitational collapse progresses, the interior density and temperature of the Sun will rise steeply, and eventually produce a braking action that stops the collapse.

The Sun's eventual collapse may take place over a span of a few million years. It is not likely that the Sun will explode, although this is far from certain. If there are any solar explosions, they will be of the nova type, not supernovas. Gradually the Sun will sink from a huge red giant star into a diameter more like the Earth's—about 12,000 kilometers. Its central temperature will reach nearly 1 billion degrees. The density at the core will go up to roughly 15,000 tons per cubic centimeter (about the volume of a sugar cube). The sun will be a white dwarf star.

Why does the gravitational collapse stop at this point? The Sun is composed of a plasma that contains ions and free electrons. As the density of the Sun increases, these particles are forced into collisions more and more frequently. Each collision produces a pressure force that tends to resist further compression. The electrons, which can be thought of as a hazy cloud rather than a firm particle, can be squeezed somewhat. But at a density of about 15,000 tons per cubic centimeter, the electrons resist further compression. The pressure forces caused by collisions among the particles now counterbalance the inward pulling force of gravity. The sun stops its collapse.

As we said before, the Sun will have gone from its present diameter of nearly 1.5 million kilometers to a size like the Earth's. Its surface temperature will actually be higher than it is now—more than 10,000°K compared to its present 6000°K. But this will be merely the last simmering of heat as the Sun collapses. Gradually the Sun will cool off, and eventually become a cold, dark body.

The Sun's demise—some 10 billion years from now—will probably be rather unspectacular. But if it is drama you want, consider the fate of more massive stars.

Neutron Stars as Pulsars

Calculations have shown that stars of more than about 1.5 times the Sun's mass do not stop their gravitational collapse when they reach the white dwarf stage. For stars of this mass, the electrons' resistance to compression fails to provide a strong enough braking force to counteract gravity. The collapse goes on.

There are a number of different possible consequences for the star. Much depends on the exact details of the star's mass, spin rate, and chemical composition. But the general outlines of the disintegration appear reasonably correct.

As the star continues to collapse, its temperature rises steeply. There may still be some unused fusable material in the star's outer layers. As it is rapidly heated up, it triggers a supernova explosion —much as the rapid heating of hydrogen in an H bomb produces a fusion explosion.

The supernova explosion blasts all the outer layers of the star off into space. Although it is hard to picture anything surviving the fantastic violence of a supernova explosion, it now seems certain that the core of the star remains relatively intact, at least for this type of supernova.

Whether or not there is a supernova explosion, the core of the star keeps on shrinking, past the density of a white dwarf. As the star's diameter keeps getting smaller and smaller, and its density gets higher and higher, gravity becomes increasingly strong. If the original star was massive enough, the gravitational force in the core eventually becomes so powerful that it can force the electrons to merge into the ions of the plasma, turning all the protons into neutrons.

We now have a star that consists of nothing but neutrons, some 10^{57} of them. The star may be about equal to the Sun's mass or heavier, but it is squeezed into a diameter of 10 to 100 kilometers. Its density is around 15 billion tons per cubic centimeter.

That is a neutron star.

If the star is not more than two solar masses, the repulsive forces that the neutrons exert on each other will resist any further gravitational collapse. The brakes are on—neutron brakes this time—and the collapse stops.

But the story does not end here. Far from it!

The star's core has collapsed to a sphere of between 10 and 100 kilometers' diameter. This happens very rapidly, in a second or so. There are still some outer layers of plasma around the core even though much of the outer material might have been blown off in one or more explosions.

This outer shell of plasma now falls in on the tiny neutron core, since gravity is always at work. The impact creates enough heat to drive the core's surface temperature up to billions of degrees for a fraction of a second. Under these circumstances, most of the heat energy is converted immediately into neutrinos. Remember that neutrinos and neutrons are two very different particles. Neutrinos have no mass, no electrical charge, and practically never interact with other particles or atoms—under ordinary circumstances.

But the conditions around a neutron star are far from ordinary. The density and temperature of the plasma around the neutron core are so high that even the aloof neutrinos can travel only a few meters before they are deflected or absorbed. Most of their enormous energy is dumped into the plasma clouds, heating the plasma to tens of billions of degrees. This causes a supernova explosion, but one that is rather different from the type we saw earlier. Some astrophysicists refer to it as a *core supernova.* The core supernova blows away all the outer layers of plasma. Nothing remains except the tiny neutron core.

All this—the collapse into the neutron core, the infall of the shell of plasma, the heating that forms the neutrinos, the core supernova explosion—happens in a few seconds.

The result? Look at the Crab Nebula, that cloud of wildly distorted plasma a few lightyears in span, still expanding at several hundred kilometers per second more than 900 years after the core supernova that produced it. And in the center of the Crab Nebula, beautifully verifying this whole theoretical story, is a pulsar.

The pulsars, most astrophysicists now believe, are rapidly rotating neutron stars.

As we saw in Chapter 5, the precisely timed radio pulses of the pulsars at first caused several astronomers to wonder if we might not be receiving signals from an intelligent race. This Little Green Men Theory, however, was soon displaced by natural explanations for the pulsars.

The theory first stated by Thomas Gold of Cornell University is the most widely accepted. Gold pictures the pulsar as a neutron star that is surrounded by fairly dense plasma clouds, probably the remainder of the core supernova. The entire complex of neutron star and plasma clouds is held together by a strong magnetic field, the same magnetic field that the star always had, but enormously intensified now by the core's compression.

If the neutron star is rotating, which it no doubt would be, its magnetic field will drag the plasma around with it. However, the further away from the surface of the neutron star you go, the faster the plasma must rotate to keep up with the forces pulling it along. This is like a "crack the whip" situation: tail end Charlie must go faster than everyone else just to stay even with the rest of the gang.

At a far enough distance, the plasma simply cannot keep up, even though it may be moving at speeds close to the speed of light. Part of the plasma snaps away from the magnetic field, and in the complex interchange of energies involved, a pulse of electromagnetic energy is formed. This happens on every rotation of the neutron star, causing a regular periodicity to the pulses. The observed timing of the pulses, all grouped around the once a second mark, fits in well with the expected spin rate of a 10 kilometer wide neutron star.

The discovery of the Crab Nebula pulsar brought enormous support to Gold's explanation. Here was exactly the situation he postulated: a neutron star imbedded in a plasma cloud laced with a strong

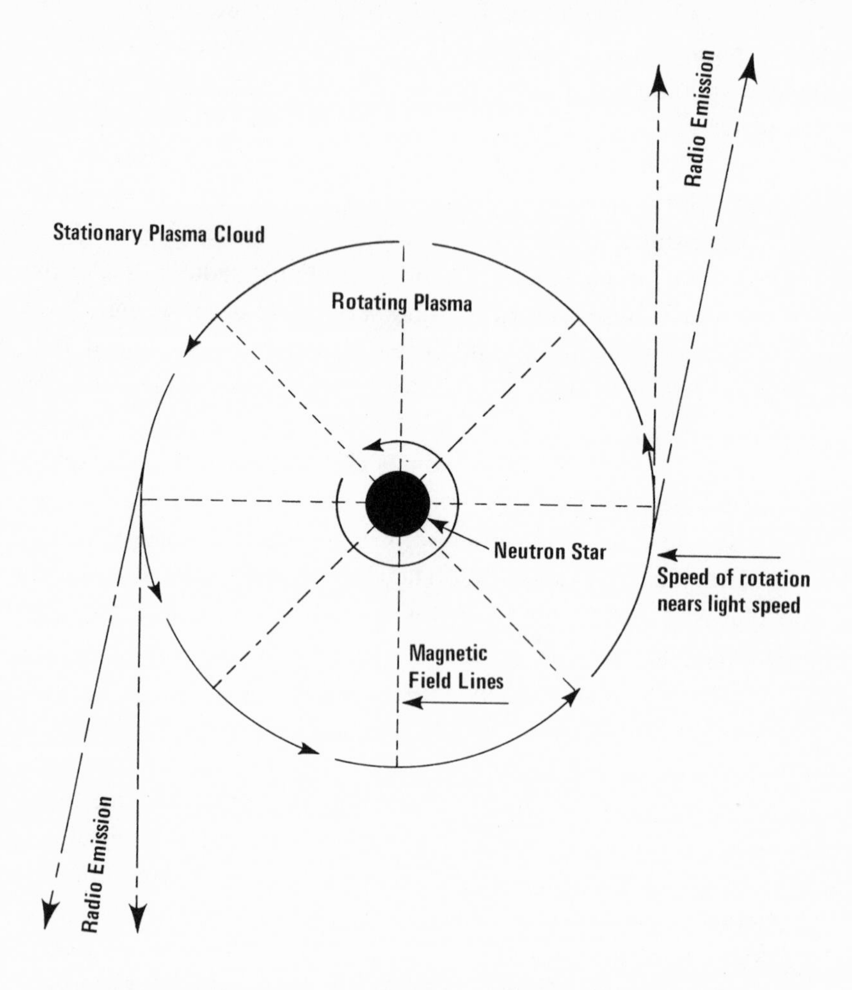

Fig. 9-5. Thomas Gold's model for a pulsar. A rapidly-spinning neutron star, linked magnetically to a plasma cloud, forces the cloud to rotate with it. At a certain distance from the star, the cloud is moving almost at lightspeed. The plasma emits bursts of electromagnetic energy at this point.

magnetic field. Early in 1969, optical pulses from the Crab pulsar were detected and photographed.

From the Crab pulsar and a few others, the periods of pulsation are gradually increasing; there is a longer time between each pulse. This probably means that the neutron star's spin rate is slowing down, as energy is transferred from the star to the plasma cloud through the magnetic field.

Is a neutron star the ultimate end of a star? Can gravitational collapse go still further?

Black Holes

The answer to those questions, according to the theoretical physicists, is that under the right circumstances a gravitational collapse can go much further. A star can literally go straight out of this universe!

Let's take another look at a neutron star. With our eyes of theory we can see through the swirling carnage of plasma that surrounds the star.

Originally a star of more than 1.5 solar masses, it has suffered a gravitational collapse, perhaps gone through either an outer shell or core supernova (or both) and now is reduced to a neutron core with a mass between 1/5 and twice the Sun's mass. For several thousand years such a neutron star will emit more x-ray energy than is emitted in the Sun's output of visible light. And as we have seen, it will also cause pulses of light and radio energy, although those pulses are coming from the plasma clouds swirling around the star, not from the neutron star itself. After 100 million years or so, the neutron star's temperature will cool down to a few thousand degrees and it will become a quiet, dark chunk of matter some 10 kilometers in diameter.

But if the neutron core of a collapsing star is more than twice the Sun's mass, its gravitational infall will not stop at the neutron star stage. It will keep on shrinking. As the interior density goes past 150 billion tons per cubic centimeter (!) the neutrons themselves are squeezed down into smaller particles called hyperons. Classical physics cannot describe what happens now: only the relativistic physics of Einstein and his followers can be used in this strange domain.

To paraphrase an old simplification, the star digs a hole, jumps in, and pulls the hole in after it!

For once the gravitational collapse goes past the neutron star stage, the star is on a one way ride to total oblivion. It will disappear from the observable universe.

If the star's neutron core is more than twice the Sun's mass, no possible braking force can stop its collapse. As the collapsing star squeezes in on itself, compressing the same amount of matter into a constantly smaller diameter, the gravitational field of the star becomes titanic. Photons emitted by the star must work against the gravitational field to escape the star's vicinity. We saw earlier that a superstar of 100 million solar masses would have a gravitational field strong enough to produce large redshifts in the photons it emits. Now we are talking about a star that is much less massive, but so compressed that its gravitational field is much stronger than a superstar's. For example, if the Sun shrank to a diameter of 5.8 kilometers, its gravitational field would be so strong that no photons could escape its surface.

For a body of the Sun's mass, the *gravitational radius* (the radius at which photons can no longer escape) is 2.9 kilometers. The Sun will never shrink to that size, or so calculations have indicated. But a neutron star of more than twice the Sun's mass will shrink to its gravitational radius. It will slide into a black hole of its own making. When such a star's diameter gets down to about 6 kilometers, it winks out. Photons can no longer escape from its surface. It disappears.

This black hole is a strange place. The gravitational collapse does not stop merely because we cannot see the star any longer. According to theory, the star keeps right on collapsing until it reaches zero volume and infinite density! Such a point is called a *Swarzschild singularity,* after the German physicist Karl Swarzschild (1873-1916).

We'll see more about the singularity aspect in a moment.

We have watched stars collapse into the white dwarf stage, explode, and collapse into neutron stars. What would it look like if we could watch the final disappearance of a star as it collapsed down into a black hole?

First, we would have to be able to see through the plasma clouds that surround the scene. Second, we would have to be able to see in x-ray wavelengths, because that is what the star is radiating. Finally, we would have to look very fast, because the whole thing happens in less than a second.

We would see the star shrinking before our x-ray sensitive eyes, and its "color" would shift toward longer wavelengths as the photons work harder and harder to get out of the ever strengthening gravity field. The star would shrink like a pricked balloon, getting smaller and "redder." Then (still within the span of a second, remember) the collapse would seem to slow down. A few photons would struggle up out of the rim of the black hole. The star finally winks out, but there is a dim halo left that is a few kilometers across, where those last few photons are taking tortuously spiralling paths to work their way out of the gravitational pit the star has dug for itself.

If there are any planets around the disappearing star, they would be quite safe from falling into the black hole, since they would be millions of kilometers away from the star. However, any native life on those planets would probably have been wiped out in the earlier stellar explosions.

If we were in a spacecraft we could approach the star quite closely—up to the gravitational radius, in fact—without being sucked into the black hole. Like a satellite orbiting Earth, our spacecraft could be under the gravitational influence of the black hole, but safe from falling into it—as long as the spacecraft maintained the proper speed and distance.

Gravitational collapse down into a black hole can also happen for objects larger than individual stars—theoretically, an entire galaxy or quasar could collapse this way. The gravitational radius for a galaxy of 1 billion stars would be roughly 1/5 of an Astronomical Unit. With a diameter of some 15 million kilometers, several such collapsed galaxies could fit inside the orbit of Mercury and we would never see them! But their gravitational effects would be horrendous, since gravitational energy *does* leak out of the black hole to affect the outside world.

In the weird world inside a black hole, where a star is crushed to zero volume and infinite density, what physical rules apply? Even relativistic physics is useless when the density gets to something like 10^{87} tons per cubic centimeter. This is 10^{78} times greater than a neutron star. If the Sun were made that dense, its size would be about 1-millionth the diameter *of an atomic nucleus.* No one knows what happens, physically, down at the bottom of a black hole.

Except that it might be bottomless. Or even openended.

Several theoreticians have pointed out that the mathematics of gravitational collapse and Swarzschild singularities apply only to perfectly spherical bodies. Stars are not perfect spheres, and galaxies are even less so. As they are gravitationally crushed, it is likely that any deformations in their shapes will be worsened, not smoothed out to spherical form. Such a non-spherical body would collapse down toward the point of a Swarzschild singularity, but it would never reach a condition of zero volume.

A body such as a star or galaxy cannot become a true Swarzschild singularity. But mathematical analysis has indicated that the body cannot stay in the same physical location where it collapsed, either. In effect, it turns the black hole into a tunnel.

You can picture this by drawing a mental image that physicists have often used to describe relativistic space-time. Picture space-time as being represented by a thin, very flexible sheet of rubber. We can envision it as a flat sheet, although actually space-time is probably curved and may be quite intricately convoluted. Massive bodies such as stars can be thought of as tiny ball bearings resting on this rubber sheet. The bigger and heavier the star, the deeper the dimple it makes in the otherwise smooth sheet.

For a star or galaxy that is collapsing into a black hole, the dimple starts to look more like a tunnel: a long, thin tube stretched in the fabric of space-time by the gravitational collapse of the massive body.

If the body does not disappear down into a singularity, then the tube-tunnel might emerge somewhere else in spacetime. The star or galaxy may dig its way out of one place in the universe and reappear somewhere and sometime else.

No one has seriously proposed working out the physics of this situation. Perhaps the enormous energy locked in the star's gravitational field is the driving force behind its tunnel digging. At the densities and gravitational field strengths involved here, it seems likely that the whole fabric of space-time can be warped.

Some cosmologists have seized on this idea to suggest that the quasars themselves might be the reemergence of collapsed galaxies, explosively bursting back into our universe after digging a tunnel through space-time.

A fantastic idea, perhaps. But no more fantastic than the quasars themselves.

The new astronomies have shown us that the universe is indeed a violent arena, far different than the placid serenity pictured during astronomy's First and Second Eras. The new astronomies of the Third Era have uncovered many staggering questions and puzzles. The answers that we eventually find should be the most exciting intellectual achievements of man.

Epilogue

A violent universe of quasars, exploding galaxies, pulsars, black holes, superstars. . . .

A solar system that looks increasingly alien and yet may harbor life on Mars, on Jupiter, even in meteoroids. . . .

The vistas of astronomy have expanded enormously in the Third Era, and are still growing as rapidly as new instruments and new ideas can be created. Our understanding of the universe is like the understanding of a child who has just gone outside his own house for the first time: there is so much to see, so much to learn!

The new discoveries are coming faster than books can be published. Fluctuating x-ray sources have been seen, but not explained. New Apollo and Mariner missions are returning fortunes of data about the Moon and Mars. Radio measurements of the quasar 3C-279 show that its two radio sources are spreading apart at a speed of 10 times the speed of light—*if* the quasar is cosmologically distant. All modern physical theory is built on the bedrock idea that nothing in the universe can travel faster than light. Is this then proof that the quasars are not cosmologically distant, that their redshifts have nothing to do with distance?

The Pioneer 10 spacecraft has been launched toward Jupiter. After flying by the giant planet, it will sweep outward, away from the solar system, the first man-made object to leave our immediate solar neighborhood.

Astronomers have also recently found galaxies that are seemingly connected by "bridges" of stars, yet each of the connected galaxies has a different redshift. If this means that the redshifts are not reliable indicators of distances, the whole fabric of modern cosmology might collapse, and entirely new theories about the size, age, and origin of the universe will be needed.

Truly, the new astronomies are expanding our consciousness of the universe we live in. And, just as truly, we are only at the beginning of astronomy's Third Era. As the old adage puts it: What is past is prologue. The best is yet to come!

Bibliography

The list of books and reports given here is not meant to be all inclusive. The broad subject matter of the new astronomies makes any attempt at a comprehensive bibliography virtually a hopeless task. So this list touches on the highlights of the points made in this book, and suggests further reading.

Up to date reports in the many fields of the new astronomies can be found in the British journal, *Nature*; in the weekly publication of the American Association for the Advancement of Science, *Science*; in *Sky and Telescope*; and in *Science News*. The bimonthly journal *Icarus* specializes in reports of solar system studies, and there are several American and international astronomical journals that give more detailed technical reports of the latest work. More general articles for the non-specialist reader can be found in the *Scientific American*, the Smithsonian Institution's *Smithsonian*, and several university news publications, such as MIT's *Technology Review*. The book *Frontiers in Astronomy*, published by W. H. Freeman and Co. (San Francisco, 1971), is a collection of several *Scientific American* articles on various aspects of the new astronomies.

Almost all the references given here are intended for the non-scientist: the general reader. More specialized and difficult references are marked with an asterisk (*).

Since the first 4 chapters of this book are mainly historical, they will be treated as one unit here, and only books will be suggested as related material.

Chapters 1 through 4

George Abell, *Exploration of the Universe,* New York: Holt, Rinehart and Winston, 1964.

Ben Bova, *In Quest of Quasars,* New York: Crowell-Collier Press, 1969.

Ben Bova, *The Fourth State of Matter,* New York: St. Martin's Press, 1971.

Gerard de Vaucouleurs, *Discovery of the Universe,* New York: Macmillan Co., 1957.

V. A. Firsoff, *Exploring the Planets,* New York: A. S. Barnes and Co., 1964.

Willy Ley, *The Conquest of Space,* New York: Viking Press, 1952.

Bernard Lovell, *Our Present Knowledge of the Universe,* Cambridge: Harvard University Press, 1967.

*Jean-Claude Pecker, *Space Observatories,* New York: Springer-Verlag New York Inc., 1970.

*Jean-Claude Pecker, *Experimental Astronomy,* New York: Springer-Verlag New York Inc., 1970.

Charles-Albert Reichen, *A History of Astronomy,* New York: The New Illustrated Library of Science and Invention, 1968.

Gilbert E. Satterthwaite, *Encyclopedia of Astronomy,* New York: St. Martin's Press, 1971.

I. S. Shklovskii and Carl Sagan, *Intelligent Life in the Universe,* New York: Holden-Day Inc., 1966.

Otto Struve, *The Universe,* Cambridge: MIT Press, 1962.

Chapter 5

Alan H. Barrett, "Radio Observations of Interstellar Hydroxyl Radicals," *Science,* vol. 157, August 25, 1967 (page 881).

Alan H. Barrett, "Radio Signals from Hydroxyl Radicals," *Scientific American,* vol. 219, no. 6, December, 1968 (page 36).

Von R. Eshelman, "Radar Astronomy," *Science,* vol. 158, November 3, 1967 (page 585).

Antony Hewish, "Pulsars," *Scientific American,* vol. 219, no. 4, October, 1968 (page 25).

*G. H. Pettinghill, C. C. Counselman, L. P. Rainville, and I. I. Shapiro, "Radar Measurements of Martian Topography, *Astronomical Journal,* vol. 74, no. 3, April, 1969 (page 461).

*James B. Pollack and David Morrison, "Venus: Determination of Atmospheric Parameters from the Microwave Spectrum," *Icarus,* vol. 12, 1970 (page 376).

S. I. Rasool, "Jupiter: 'Rosetta Stone' of the Solar System," *Astronautics and Aeronautics,* October, 1968 (page 24).

Irwin I. Shapiro, "Radar Observations of the Planets," *Scientific American,* vol. 219, no. 1, July, 1968 (page 28).

Dietrick E. Thomsen, "Microwaves from the Planets," *Science News,* vol. 99, no. 25, June 19, 1971 (page 424).

Gerald L. Wick, "Interstellar Molecules: Chemicals in the Sky," *Science,* vol. 170, October 9, 1970 (page 149).

Chapter 6

John N. Bahcall, "Neutrinos from the Sun," *Scientific American,* vol. 221, no. 1, July, 1969 (page 28).

Charles A. Barth and Charles W. Hord, "Mariner Ultraviolet Spectrometer: Topography and Polar Cap," *Science,* vol. 173, July 16, 1971 (page 197).

*G. G. Fazio, "High-Energy Gamma-Ray Astronomy," *Nature,* vol. 225, March 7, 1970 (page 905).

P. A. Feldman, M. J. Rees, and M. W. Werner, "Infrared and Microwave Astronomy," *Nature,* vol. 224, November 22, 1964 (page 752).

Riccardo Giacconi, "X-Ray Stars," *Scientific American,* vol. 217, no. 6, December, 1967 (page 36).

V. L. Ginzburg, "The Astrophysics of Cosmic Rays," *Scientific American,* vol. 220, no. 2, February, 1969 (page 50).

Leo Goldberg, "Ultraviolet Astronomy," *Scientific American,* vol. 220, no. 6, June, 1969 (page 92).

Allen H. Hammond, "Ultraviolet Astronomy: Progress with the OAO," *Science,* vol. 170, November 27, 1970 (page 960).

Harold L. Johnson, "Infrared Stars," *Science,* vol. 157, August 11, 1967 (page 615).

Frank J. Low, "Infrared Astrophysics," *Science,* Vol. 164, May 2, 1969 (page 501).

G. Negebauer and Robert B. Leighton, "The Infrared Sky," *Scientific American,* vol. 219, no. 2, August, 1968 (page 51).

Frederick Reines and J. P. F. Sellschop, "Neutrinos from the Atmosphere and Beyond," *Scientific American,* vol. 214, no. 2, February, 1966 (page 40).

Joseph Weber, "The Detection of Gravitational Waves," *Scientific American,* vol. 224, no. 5, May, 1971 (page 22).

A. W. Wolfendale, "Cosmic Rays in Gold Mines," *Nature,* vol. 219, September 21, 1968 (page 1215).

Chapter 7

Laurence J. Cahill Jr., "The Magnetosphere," *Scientific American*, vol. 212, no. 3, March, 1965 (page 58).

*John R. Cronin and Carleton B. Moore, "Amino Acid Analyses of the Murchison, Murray and Allende Carbonaceous Chondrites," *Science*, vol. 172, June 25, 1971 (page 1327).

Palmer Dyal and Curtis W. Parkin, "The Magnetism of the Moon," *Scientific American,* vol. 225, no. 2, August, 1971 (page 62).

Von R. Eshelman, "The Atmospheres of Mars and Venus," *Scientific American,* vol. 220, no. 3, March, 1969 (page 79).

Ellis Levin, Donald D. Vicle and Lowell B. Eldenkamp, "The Lunar Orbiter Missions to the Moon," *Scientific American,* vol. 218, no. 5, May, 1968 (page 59).

J. N. James, "The Voyage of Mariner IV," *Scientific American,* vol. 214, no. 3, March, 1966 (page 42).

Robert B. Leighton, "The Photographs from Mariner IV," *Scientific American*, vol. 214, no. 4, April, 1966 (page 54).

Robert B. Leighton, "The Surface of Mars," *Scientific American*, vol. 222, no. 5, May, 1970 (page 26).

Bartholomew Nagy, *et al.*, "Carbon Compounds in Apollo 12 Lunar Samples," *Nature,* vol. 232, July 9, 1971 (page 94).

National Aeronautics and Space Administration, "Apollo 11 Preliminary Science Report," *NASA SP-214,* 1969.

National Aeronautics and Space Administration, "Mariner-Mars 1969, a Preliminary Report," *NASA SP-225,* 1969.

National Aeronautics and Space Administration, "Apollo 12 Preliminary Science Report," *NASA SP-235,* 1970.

*S. I. Rasool and C. de Bergh, "The Runaway Greenhouse and the Accumulation of CO_2 in the Venus Atmosphere," *Nature,* vol. 226, June 13, 1970 (page 1037).

Richard K. Sloan, "The Scientific Experiments of Mariner IV," *Scientific American*, vol. 214, no. 5, May, 1966 (page 62).

Kurt R. Stehling, "Balloon Astronomy, A Case for More," *Smithsonian*, vol. 2, no. 3, June, 1971 (page 28).

George W. Wetherill, "Of Time and the Moon," *Science*, vol. 173, July 30, 1971 (page 383).

James A. Wood, "The Lunar Soil," *Scientific American*, vol. 223, no. 2, August, 1970 (page 14).

Chapter 8

Hannes Alfven, "Plasma Physics, Space Research, and the Origin of the Solar System," *Science*, vol. 172, June 4, 1971 (page 991).

*Bevan M. French, "How Did Venus Lose Its Angular Momentum?" *Science*, vol. 173, July 9, 1971 (page 169).

*Carl Sagan and Joseph Veverka, "The Microwave Spectrum of Mars: An Analysis," *Icarus*, vol. 14, no. 2, April, 1971 (page 222).

National Aeronautics and Space Administration, "Planetology 1958-1964," *NASA SP-99*, 1966.

Brian Mason, "The Lunar Rocks," *Scientific American*, vol. 225, no. 4, October, 1971 (page 48).

Chapter 9

Allen L. Hammond, "Stellar Old Age: White Dwarfs, Neutron Stars, and Black Holes," *Science*, vol. 171, March 12, March 19, and March 26, 1971 (pages 994, 1133 and 1228, respectively).

Stephen P. Maran, "In Nine Centuries, Search Unravels Many Parts of the Crab Nebula Mystery," *Smithsonian*, vol. 1, no. 3, June, 1970.

W. H. McCrea, "Cosmology after Half a Century," *Science*, vol. 160, June 21, 1968 (page 1295).

P. J. E. Peebles and David Wilkinson, "The Primeval Fireball," *Scientific American*, vol. 216, no. 6, June, 1967 (page 28).

Kip S. Thorne, "The Death of a Star," *Science Year 1968*, Field Enterprises Educational Corporation, 1968.

Index